Part 1

Using Assessment

Contents

INTRODUCTION

This Assessment Book includes information about assessment in McGraw-Hill's **Adventures in Time and Place,** directions for administering and scoring Chapter Tests, Unit Tests, and Performance Assessments, blackline masters, and answer keys.

Description of the Assessments

There are two types of assessments provided in this book for *Ancient World*: paper-and-pencil Chapter Tests and Unit Tests, and Performance Assessments for each chapter and unit.

Part 3 has **Chapter Test** blackline masters for each chapter in *Ancient World* and **Unit Test** blackline masters for each unit. Each Chapter Test comprises three sections:

- The **Content** section has 10 test questions, or items, about the content of the chapter. Five of the items are multiple-choice questions and five are short-answer questions — fill-in, matching, written response.

- The **Skills** section has 5 short-answer items for each skill taught in the chapter.

- The **Writing** section has two essay questions measuring both the content and skills in the chapter. The essay questions include a visual stimulus and require the student to write a brief paragraph.

Each Unit Test comprises two sections: a **Content and Skills** section with 10 multiple-choice items and 10 short-answer items measuring the content and skills taught in all of the chapters in the unit, and a **Writing** section with two essay questions measuring both the content and skills in the unit.

Answer Keys for all Chapter Tests and Unit Tests appear in sequence in Part 2.

Part 4 provides **Performance Assessments** for each chapter and each unit in *Ancient World*. There are three Chapter Performance Assessments in each chapter, based on the three *Think and Write* activities in the Chapter Review of the Pupil's Edition. Each of these activities results in a piece of writing, such as a journal entry or a letter.

Each Unit Performance Assessment is based on the Unit Project in the Unit Review of the Pupil's Edition. Each unit project results in a product that can be assessed. It also involves a process that can be evaluated through observation.

Each Performance Assessment provides guidelines for using the assessment. It includes the following:

- A statement of the **goal** of the activity or project

- **Suggestions** for modeling and instruction that will enable students to complete the activity or project

- **Portfolio Opportunities** that provide suggestions for evaluating student performance—including self-assessment and peer assessment—and incorporating the assessment into a portfolio

- A **Scoring Rubric** designed to help teachers evaluate each student's performance and score it as Excellent, Good, Fair, Poor, or Unscorable

Principles of Assessment

Assessment in *Adventures in Time and Place* involves the use of multiple measures in a wide variety of authentic situations to evaluate what students can do. Information collected through various forms of assessment is used for evaluation or making judgments about student performance. Forms of assessment provided with this program include both paper-and-pencil tests and performance assessments. Our approach to assessment is based on the following principles.

Assessment should be closely integrated with instruction.

It should be based on the goals of instruction, and it should measure what is taught, in the way in which it is taught.

Assessment should be based on the notion of *progress*—evaluating student progress toward achieving the goals and objectives of instruction.

It should be based on the ability to apply critical thinking strategies in a variety of contexts, not only on mastering isolated skills.

Assessment should be continuous, throughout the school year, and should incorporate a wide variety of modes and types of assessment.

Frequent assessments will provide formative information that is useful in guiding instruction. A wide variety of assessments will provide a comprehensive profile of each student.

Assessment tasks and activities should be direct and authentic, reflecting what students actually need to be able to do.

Assessment in authentic situations requires real-life tasks, which may involve any number of activities, from everyday classroom observations to student work samples to independent projects.

Authentic assessment activities should integrate social studies curriculum with all of the language arts: reading, writing, listening, speaking, and viewing.

Language arts are integrated in every aspect of real life, and they should be integrated in the classroom.

Assessment should include self-assessment and cooperative efforts between teacher and students, among student peers, and involving parents.

Students can learn a great deal from understanding and applying the standards of good work to their own achievements.

The assessments provided with this program are based on these principles of assessment. The Chapter Tests, Unit Tests, and Performance Assessments are intended to be administered at the end of each chapter and each unit. They are designed to help you determine how well students have mastered the content of the chapter or unit and how well they can apply the skills taught in the chapter or unit. Other ways of using tests, performance assessments, and portfolios with this program are described on the next page.

Assessment: Questions and Answers

Can the Chapter Tests be used in different ways?

Yes. The Chapter Tests have three sections: Content, Skills, and Writing. You may choose to give any or all of these sections when you administer the test, and you may use the sections of the test in other ways. For example, you might decide to use the Content section as a test and the Skills and Writing sections for instructional practice or follow-up instruction.

How can I use performance assessments with this program?

There are three general approaches to using performance assessment with this program. First, you can observe students in the classroom—during everyday activities and in specific activities outlined in the Teacher's Edition. Second, you can administer the Performance Assessments for each chapter and unit. Third, you can use portfolios.

How do I use the Performance Assessments?

When you have completed a chapter or unit, use the Performance Assessment guidelines in Part 4 to help prepare students to complete the activity or project and evaluate their performance. Each Performance Assessment offers suggestions for introducing the activity or project and assisting students in its completion, suggestions for using the assessment as a portfolio opportunity, and a scoring rubric for evaluating student performance.

What is portfolio assessment?

Simply stated, a portfolio is an organized collection of a student's work. A portfolio system can be as simple as a set of folders and a box to keep them in, but portfolio assessment is much more than that: it is a powerful concept for developing a comprehensive profile of each student.

How do I get started with portfolios?

Start with something simple and easy to manage. Introduce portfolios to the students as a way to organize their work. Tell them that they will be choosing their best works to put into the portfolio. At the beginning of the year, you may want to model the process by showing them your own portfolio or inviting guests, such as artists or photographers, to come in and show students their portfolios.

How do I involve students in portfolios?

Involving students is a critical part of portfolio assessment. Tell students they are responsible for taking care of their own portfolios. Talk with students to set goals for each unit and for the year. Work with them to choose their best works to help them meet their goals. Have students evaluate their own works by writing notes or completing self-assessments for each work they put into the portfolio. Periodically, have a portfolio review conference with students to look at what they have done, help them assess their own progress, and set new goals for the next unit.

How can I figure out students' grades from these assessment materials?

The tests are designed to be scored by section, and the score for each section can be converted to a percentage score for grading purposes. For the Writing section of each test and for the Performance Assessments, the student's performance can be scored on a 4-point scale. This type of score can also be converted to a percentage score for grading, as explained in the following pages.

Administering Assessments

The Chapter Tests, Unit Tests, and Performance Assessments are designed to be used with each chapter and unit. Before administering these assessments, familiarize yourself with the assessments themselves and the guidelines in this Teacher's Manual.

Administering Chapter and Unit Tests
The **Chapter Tests** and **Unit Tests** in Part 3 are designed for group administration. You may choose to administer the complete test or any of its parts.

These tests are not intended to be timed. Students should be given ample time to complete the tests. However, for planning purposes, the chart below shows the estimated time required to administer the sections of each kind of test.

Section	Number of Items	Estimated Time
Chapter Test		
Content	10	10–15 minutes
Skills	5 or 10	10–15 minutes
Writing	2 prompts	20–30 minutes
Unit Test		
Content and Skills	20	20–30 minutes
Writing	2 prompts	20–30 minutes

Depending on the needs of your students, you may decide to administer the entire test in one sitting, or you may administer sections of the test in separate sittings.

To administer a test, give a copy of the test to each student. Have students write their names at the top of each page. Directions for students appear at the top of each page. Have students read the directions, read the questions, and mark or write their answers on the test pages.

For multiple-choice items, students fill in the circle before the correct answer to each item. For short-answer questions, students write a letter, a word, a phrase, or a sentence on the lines provided. For each Writing prompt, students write a brief paragraph on the lines provided.

During the administration, check to see that each student is following the directions, is answering the right items, and is marking responses correctly.

Administering Performance Assessments
In Part 4 of this manual, you will find **Performance Assessments** for each chapter and each unit in *Ancient World*. Each Performance Assessment is one page intended for the teacher's use. The Chapter Performance Assessments are based on the Think and Write activities in the Chapter Review, and the Performance Assessment for each unit is based on the Unit Project in the Unit Review.

The Performance Assessments work in tandem with the Think and Write activities or Unit Projects to provide both instruction and assessment. When you have completed a chapter or unit, use the Performance Assessments to help prepare students to complete the Think and Write activity or Unit Project and then to evaluate their performance.

First, explain to students what they will be doing in the activity or project.

Second, use the suggestions at the top of the Performance Assessment page to introduce the activity or project and review instructional material from the chapter or unit.

Third, explain to students what is expected of them and how their work will be evaluated through the Performance Assessment.

Scoring

The Chapter Tests and Unit Tests are designed to be scored by section. Chapter Tests have three sections (Content, Skills, Writing) and Unit Tests have two sections (Content and Skills, Writing). For each test the correct responses are listed in the Answer Key (found in Part 2 of this manual).

For multiple-choice questions, the letter of the correct response is listed in the Answer Key. For short-answer items (such as fill-in-the-blank or matching), the correct letter, word, or phrase is listed.

In some cases where questions require the students to supply their own answers in phrases or sentences, the Answer Key provides the expected response or the factual information required. However, the content and wording of the students' answers may vary from what is listed in the Answer Key. In these cases the Answer Key should be used only as a guideline for determining whether students' responses are correct or not.

Scoring Tests: Content and Skills

To score the Content and Skills sections, use the Answer Key to mark each answer correct or incorrect. To determine a score for each section, add up the number of items answered correctly (for example, 3 of 5, 7 of 10, or 16 of 20).

To find a percentage score, divide the number answered correctly by the total number of items. Examples

$3 \div 5 = .60$, or 60%
$7 \div 10 = .70$, or 70%
$16 \div 20 = .80$, or 80%

Scoring Tests: Writing

To score the Writing section, use the Answer Key to evaluate each student's responses. The Answer Key describes the characteristics of an *Excellent* response and an *Adequate* response for each question. You may score the student's response as Excellent, Adequate, or Not Adequate based on the criteria listed in the Answer Key. Or, you may want to rate each of the student's responses on a 4-point scale, as explained on the next page.

Passing Scores

The Chapter Tests and Unit Tests are based on the content and skills taught in the chapter or the unit and are scored in relation to a criterion, or passing, score. In the Content and Skills sections, the recommended passing score is 70% (4 of 5, 7 of 10, or 14 of 20 items answered correctly). For the Writing section, students should achieve a score of at least *adequate* on each question, or at least 2 on the 4-point scale. (These are recommended passing scores; you may want to adjust them upward or downward for your students.)

Alternative Scoring Method for Writing: Using a 4-Point Scale

For the Writing section of each test, responses are intended to be scored as *Excellent, Adequate,* or *Not Adequate*. However, you may want to use an alternative method of scoring each student's responses on a scale of 1–4 (or 0 for an unscorable response). Each response may be awarded zero to four points depending on its accuracy and completeness. For example, students who provide a partial response to an exercise might receive one point, while students who give a full and outstanding response would receive four points. (A student who does not respond to a question or whose response is for some reason unscorable would receive zero points.)

To score students' responses on a 4-point scale, use the rating scale defined below. If you wish to convert scores on the 4-point scale to percentage scores, add the scores from both questions (for example, $2 + 3 = 5$) and then use this conversion chart.

Conversion Chart	
Number of Points	**Percentage Score**
1	13%
2	25%
3	38%
4	50%
5	63%
6	75%
7	88%
8	100%

4-Point Rating Scale

4 Excellent. The student makes an outstanding response that includes all or most of the elements listed in the Answer Key. This score indicates that the student not only understands the necessary information and concepts but also exhibits additional insight into their meaning and importance.

3 Good. The student makes an above-average response that includes many of the elements listed in the Answer Key for both an adequate and an excellent response, indicating that the student has a firm grasp of the necessary concepts and information.

2 Fair. The student makes a satisfactory response that includes the elements listed in the Answer Key for an adequate response, indicating that the student has satisfactory knowledge and understanding of the necessary concepts and information.

1 Poor. The student makes a minimal response that does not include the elements listed in the Answer Key for an adequate response, indicating that the student has not learned or does not understand the necessary concepts and information.

0 No Response. The student did not respond to the exercise, or the response is illegible or for some other reason unscorable.

Scoring Performance Assessments

Each Performance Assessment includes a scoring rubric designed to help you evaluate each student's performance. The rubric describes the characteristics of the project on a 4-point scale: Excellent, Good, Fair, Poor (or Unscorable). Use the scoring rubric to score each student's work as a 4, 3, 2, 1, or 0. (In percentage scores, 4 = 100%, 3 = 75%, 2 = 50%, 1 = 25%.)

Portfolio Assessment Opportunities

The Performance Assessments are ideal activities for self assessment, peer assessment, and inclusion in a portfolio. The "Portfolio Opportunity" guidelines suggest ways to engage students in evaluating their own work through self-assessment or peer assessment before displaying their work or placing it in their portfolios.

Self-Assessment and Peer Assessment

Students can learn a great deal from understanding and applying the standards of good work to their own achievements. In using the Performance Assessments, encourage students to assess their own work by pointing out what they think is good about it and what they think they might do better next time. You might want to have them complete the Self-Assessment Checklist on page T9 after they have completed a Think and Write activity or Unit Project (or other type of project activity).

When students have become familiar with self-assessment, have them practice peer assessment by working with partners. Encourage students to assess the work of others by pointing out positive aspects of it and discussing what they think is good about the other student's work. You may want to model this process for students so they understand the positive tone that should be applied. You might want to have them complete the Peer Assessment Checklist on page T10 to assess a student's work, a partner's work, or a group's work on a Think and Write activity, Unit Project, or other activity.

Group Assessment

In many projects and activities, students will be working with partners or in groups. To assess an individual's performance in a group situation, you can gather information through observation of the students as they work, through conferences with students in which they discuss their work, through self-assessments, and through peer assessments. You may want to use the Group Assessment Chart on page T11 to help evaluate and record individual performances.

Class Summary Chart

To develop a profile of student performance on the assessments for each unit, you may want to record the Unit Test and Unit Performance Assessment scores on the Class Summary Chart on page T12. From the student's test scores and Performance Assessment results, you can determine an overall rating of the student's performance for each unit. This overall rating may be expressed on the 4-point scale, as a percentage score, or as a letter grade.

Self-Assessment Checklist

Name _____ **Date** _____

Activity or Project _____

1. What did you do in this activity or project?

   _____

   _____

2. What parts of the activity or project did you do well?

   _____

   _____

3. What could you do better next time to improve your work?

   _____

   _____

4. What did you learn from this activity or project?

   _____

   _____

5. What did you like best about this activity or project?

   _____

   _____

Peer Assessment Checklist

Name _____ **Date** _____

Activity or Project _____

1. What did your classmate do in this activity or project?

   _____

   _____

2. If you worked with your classmate on this activity, tell what parts you did. (If you did not work with your classmate, skip to question 3.)

   _____

   _____

3. What was the best thing your classmate did?

   _____

   _____

   _____

4. How would you rate your classmate's work? (Circle one)

   Excellent   Good   Fair   Needs Improvement

5. What suggestions would you make to help your classmate do better next time?

   _____

   _____

   _____

Group Assessment Chart

Class _____ Activity or Project _____

Directions. Rate each individual's performance as 4, 3, 2, 1, or 0 on each of the criteria listed below. (4 = Excellent, 3 = Good, 2 = Fair, 1 = Poor, 0 = Unscorable)

Student Names																						
Criteria																						
Participates in group work																						
Contributes to project success																						
Listens to others																						
Asks and answers questions																						
Stays on task																						
Cooperates with others																						
Offers positive suggestions																						
Exhibits leadership																						
Compliments and encourages others																						
Overall Rating																						

CLASS SUMMARY CHART

Class _____ Unit _____

Student Name	Unit Test: Content and Skills	Unit Test: Writing	Performance Assessment	Overall Rating

Part 2

Answer Key

Contents

CHAPTER 1

Content

1. a
2. d
3. b
4. c
5. c

6. physical region
7. political region
8. cultural value
9. English
10. representative democracy

Skills

1. 35°N, 90°W
2. Alberta and Saskatchewan
3. Kansas and Nebraska
4. Florida; 25°N, 80°W
5. Oregon, California, and Nevada

Writing

1. An adequate response will describe the five climate regions of Australia with some indication of their location. (Example: The northernmost parts of Australia have a tropical climate. The central part of Australia has desert and semi-dry climate regions. Two parts of the southern coast have a warm and rainy climate with a dry summer, and the eastern coast has a warm and rainy climate.) An excellent response will also describe the kinds of weather most likely to be found in these climate regions. (Examples: The tropical region is hot and humid. The desert and semi-dry regions are hot and dry.)

2. An adequate response will explain that culture is a people's way of life, while customs are things that people practice regularly. It will also give at least one example of each. For example, many of the peoples of Latin America share a common culture because they speak Spanish and share the same religion. Examples of customs might include types of food that people eat, how they dress, holidays they celebrate, and religious practices. An excellent response will further explain that culture is largely based on a people's beliefs, values, and ethnic heritage, and customs are daily or regular habits that reflect cultural values. Also, all cultures are made up of many different customs.

CHAPTER 2

Content

1. d
2. a
3. c
4. b
5. c

6. d
7. c
8. b
9. e
10. a

Skills

1. He needed to find out where the old coins came from.
2. He looked at maps in the library.
3. He looked for landmarks. Then he remembered the park was very old.
4. He found that a bank once stood where his house is located.
5. Answers will vary.

Writing

1. An adequate response will mention at least one example of oral tradition and at least one primary source, and it will explain how these sources helped Madden. An excellent response will cite more examples of oral tradition and primary sources. Examples: The family stories were oral tradition. They gave him basic information and the clues needed to start his research. The historic documents (freedom papers, birth certificates, letters) were primary sources. They helped prove that the stories were true.
2. An adequate response will tell whether *We Were Always Free* would be a good source or not and give supporting reasons. An excellent response will consider both sides of the argument, make a decision one way or another, and support the decision with several examples. Points in favor of *We Were Always Free* as a source include its basis in fact and the number of years of history it covers. A point against it is that it tells one family's story from one point of view.

Content and Skills

1. b
2. a
3. a
4. c
5. d
6. b
7. d
8. a
9. b
10. d

11. b
12. d
13. a
14. c
15. physical
16. about 10°N, 70°W
17. mountains
18. archaeology
19. viewpoint
20. prehistory

Writing

1. An adequate response should note that each of these artifacts comes from a different time period, and that books and periodicals in the library would be the next logical step in attempting to discover when each of these artifacts was once used. An excellent response would note that each of these artifacts is a primary source from the time period in which it was used. After researching the age of the artifacts in secondary sources such as books or magazines, students would attempt to ask older adults for personal anecdotes about each of the artifacts.

2. An adequate response will indicate that the student would set a goal, consider alternatives, and make a decision. An excellent response will apply these steps to the question of whether or not to work at an archaeological dig for the summer.

CHAPTER 3

Content

1. a
2. b
3. d
4. c
5. b

6. b
7. e
8. c
9. a
10. d

Skills

1. It shows when *Homo erectus*, Neanderthals, and modern *Homo sapiens* lived on Earth.
2. one million years
3. *Homo erectus*

4. Yes. Neanderthals still existed when *Homo sapiens* appeared 40,000 years ago. They both lived on Earth until Neanderthals disappeared 35,000 years ago.
5. approximately 250,000 years ago

Writing

1. An adequate response will note that *Homo habilis* people apparently lived only in Africa, while *Homo erectus* people lived in Africa, Europe, and Asia. In Africa, both peoples lived in the same area near Olduvai Gorge. An excellent response will explain these observations. Examples: *Homo erectus* people could migrate successfully from Africa to Europe and Asia because they could build fires to keep themselves warm in these colder climates. *Homo habilis* people probably did not know how to make fire, so they could not survive outside Africa.

2. An adequate response will note that the people who made these objects were tool users since they made a stone blade; they were probably also hunters since they made arrowheads as well as a necklace of animal teeth and bones. An excellent response will note that a necklace shows that the people who made it valued beauty, and it suggests that the people may have been modern *Homo sapiens*.

CHAPTER 4

Content

1. c
2. a
3. b
4. d
5. a

6. agriculture
7. specialization
8. civilization
9. terraces
10. revolution

Skills

1. a
2. b
3. a
4. b
5. b

6. To compare the populations of world regions in 1850.
7. The size of each region represents its population rather than its land area.
8. In 1850, it was the region with the largest population.
9. Europe had more people than North America in 1850.
10. South America. It is the smallest region on the cartogram.

Writing

1. An adequate response will note that Catal Huyuk was located in an area where both wheat and barley grew wild, and it will suggest that these conditions helped hunters and gatherers discover and develop agriculture which could support a large population. An excellent response will include more detail and show a greater awareness of how agriculture led to specialization and trade in a permanent community.

2. An adequate response will state a choice and give at least one reason which reflects understanding of advantages and disadvantages of each way of life. Example: The group would choose to continue hunting and gathering because farmers were often less healthy than hunter-gathers. They caught illnesses easily in permanent settlements, and they suffered from poor nutrition when their crop failed. An excellent response will provide several reasons and show a greater understanding of each way of life.

Content and Skills

1. b
2. b
3. a
4. c
5. d
6. a
7. c
8. d
9. c
10. b
11. 6,000 years
12. cattle domesticated
13. 3,000 years
14. No. The abbreviation *c.* means "about" or "around."
15. No. The first crops were planted around 9000 B.C., 5,000 years before the plow was invented in 4000 B.C.
16. theory
17. Border Cave
18. revolution
19. Catal Huyuk
20. specialization

Writing

1. An adequate response will note one aspect of the physical environment, explain how it influenced Old Stone Age people, and explain how these people began to control it. Example: The earliest people of the Old Stone Age lived only in areas with mild climates because they could not survive in cold climates. But as people learned to control fire and develop tools for building and sewing, they could survive in colder climates by using fire for heat, building protective shelters, and making warm clothes. An excellent response will relate other advances that demonstrate early humans' increasing control over their environment, such as hunting with bows and arrows and using language to communicate and solve problems.

2. An adequate response will note that the people who lived in this settlement raised grain and animals (indicated by the grain storage area and animal pens), had developed a religion (indicated by the temple), and had begun to develop specialization, or crafts (indicated by the workshops). An excellent response will connect these observations to other concepts and/or include more complex observations and speculations. Examples: The existence of agriculture and specialization indicates a New Stone Age (or later) site; the orderly arrangement of the public buildings suggests cooperation and planning in constructing the settlement.

CHAPTER 5

Content

1. b
2. b
3. a
4. c
5. a

6. Hammurabi
7. Nebuchadnezzar
8. Gilgamesh
9. Sargon
10. Enheduana

Skills

1. They had plenty of materials for making clay, or they did not have any other materials for building.
2. They were used to form walls.
3. The sun-dried bricks eventually crumbled.
4. They made long-lasting walls.
5. Parts of the ziggurats they built have lasted four thousand years.

Writing

1. An adequate response will mention that the people of Mesopotamia developed a system of writing and a code of laws, and they invented both the wheel and irrigation. An excellent response will mention less obvious contributions, such as the development of schools, literature, and science.
2. An adequate response will indicate that most of the population lives in the lower plains along the major rivers and will give a logical reason. For example, towns and cities tend to prosper in areas where there is plenty of food, and farmers in Iraq are much more likely to succeed along the rivers than in other areas. An excellent response will provide more detail. For example, it might indicate that the population would be considerably smaller in the mountains where the soil is poor or in the desert where there is no water for crops. It might also refer to ancient Mesopotamia and the fact that it developed between the Tigris and Euphrates rivers, which still provide water and transportation.

CHAPTER 6

Content

1. d
2. a
3. b
4. c
5. d

6. c
7. b
8. e
9. a
10. d

Skills

1. about 400 miles
2. about 1 1/2 miles, or 2 kilometers
3. Luxor or Aswan
4. It can show more detailed information.
5. the small-scale map (Egypt: the Nile Valley)

Writing

1. An adequate response will explain that hieroglyphs were used for recording taxes and making calculations. These uses changed Egyptian culture by making complex accounting possible and by extending government control over its people. An excellent response will mention other uses of hieroglyphs (such as, writing letters and recording medical procedures and treatments). It will also explain other ways in which the use of hieroglyphs changed Egyptian culture. For example, it made possible the building of the pyramids, communicating over long distances, developing sophisticated medical knowledge, and inventing a calendar.

2. An adequate response will specify that the best farmland can be found along the Nile River, especially in the delta area of Lower Egypt, and will tell why. For example, the river brings down silt to fertilize the land and water for irrigating fields. An excellent response will also analyze the potential of other areas. For example, the land around Lake Nasser does not receive the benefits of flooding, but at least there is water. Much of the rest of Egypt is desert that offers neither good soil nor water.

CHAPTER 7

Content

1. a
2. b
3. c
4. b
5. c

6. b
7. d
8. e
9. c
10. a

Skills

1. c
2. b
3. a
4. c
5. b

Writing

1. An adequate response will describe at least one similarity and at least one difference between the kingdom of Kush and the Nok culture. Examples of similarities: These civilizations both developed in river valleys. People in both civilizations depended on farming, worked with iron, and influenced other cultures. Examples of differences: We know more about Kush than about Nok. People of the Nok culture worked with tin in addition to iron; the people of Kush traded with other cultures, had a social pyramid, and were apparently a powerful kingdom. An excellent response will provide more detail. Examples: The farmers of Kush raised barley and millet, while the farmers of Nok raised sorghum. The people of Nok made terra cotta figures. The people of Kush had numerous luxury goods, such as gold and ivory.

2. An adequate response will identify at least one physical feature (such as location on a plain or plateau, proximity to a river), a natural resource (such as fertile soil, timber, minerals, abundant wildlife or vegetation for food), and an aspect of climate (moderate temperatures, adequate rainfall) that would support the development of agriculture and other activities to support a civilization. An excellent response will provide more detail and show a greater understanding of how the physical environment affects the development and progress of civilizations.

Content and Skills

1. d
2. b
3. a
4. b
5. b
6. c
7. b
8. d
9. b
10. d

11. Nubia
12. smelt
13. Fertile Crescent
14. Tigris
15. scribes
16. Memphis
17. silt
18. papyrus
19. Kerma
20. drought

Writing

1. An adequate response will describe how, during the New Kingdom period, Egypt reconquered the territory of Nubia and gained control of the ancient and wealthy kingdom of Kush. The response will go on to describe how this expansion of Egypt added great wealth to its empire, giving it access to raw materials such as gold, precious stones, ivory and ebony, and animal skins. An excellent response will further describe the interaction by noting how control of Kush gave Egypt access to rich trade routes to other African kingdoms even farther to the south. The response may also describe how Egyptian craftworkers used the raw materials to create beautiful objects of art, such as furniture, jewelry, and other fine goods for the pharaoh and other wealthy families.

2. An adequate response will accurately describe the roles of two of the groups in the Egyptian social pyramid. Examples: the Pharaoh was the ruler of the society; the large numbers of farmers and slaves performed agricultural work, such as digging canals. An excellent response will go on to make conclusions from how the chart is organized. A person's position in society depended on what he or she did for a living. The pharaoh's being at the top indicates that he was the sole ruler, and that farmers and slaves were at the bottom indicates that they made up the largest part of society.

CHAPTER 8

Content

1. d
2. b
3. a
4. b
5. c

6. caste
7. dharma
8. monk
9. Vedas
10. Buddhism

Skills

1. farming
2. forest land
3. Deccan Plateau
4. barley, sugarcane
5. The Thar Desert is in the northwest, and the Himalayas are found far north.

Writing

1. An adequate response should indicate the similarity between the importance of food and cotton production in ancient times and modern times. An excellent response will address each of the industries in the chart. Example: As in ancient times, Pakistani farmers grow food to feed their families. Cotton was and is a very important crop. Residents of the ancient cities were also involved with weaving cloth from cotton. The industries of fertilizer production, cigarette making, carpet making, and steel production were not a part of ancient life, although metalworkers did exist. Other craftworkers existed, just as part of the population in modern Pakistan works in manufacturing.

2. An adequate response will mention at least three features of life in the Indus Valley. Example: In the Indus Valley, farmers were usually able to use irrigation to grow two crops each year. Animals were domesticated and their use enabled farmers to plow larger fields. Cotton was grown and used to make cloth for the first time. An excellent response will detail other crops, such as rice, bananas, black pepper, mustard, and sesame. It will also note that farming began in the Indus Valley around 6000 B.C.

CHAPTER 9

Content

1. d
2. c
3. a
4. b
5. a

6. Wudi
7. Confucius
8. Fu Hao
9. Shihuangdi
10. Han Gaozu

Skills

1. "To help his people understand one another, an emperor named Shihuangdi set up a single system of writing that everyone in his empire could read."

2. It helped unite the people, and it has helped China endure for centuries.

3. "It does not have an alphabet. In an alphabet each character stands for a sound."

4. It explains why people in China do not always understand one another.

5. Example: Shihuangdi developed a standard written form of Chinese so that people across his empire could communicate with one another.

Writing

1. An adequate response will describe how during the Han dynasty, emperors adopted some of the ideas of Confucianism, such as the view that a subject must respect the ruler, but the ruler must be wise and good. Han emperors also wanted to lessen the power of nobles and rule fairly. An excellent response will explain how the Han emperor Wudi created schools to prepare people for government service, so educated people—not just nobles—got government jobs.

2. An adequate response will explain that control of the rivers was important because the rivers made farming successful and served as protective geographic boundaries. An excellent response will explain these reasons in more detail. For example, the success of farming was important because it allowed for greater population and more farmers to help build and defend the growing empire. It may also mention that control of the rivers allowed rulers to control trade and transportation in and out of the empire.

CHAPTER 10

Content

1. a
2. d
3. c
4. c
5. b

6. tropical
7. totem
8. rain forest
9. earthwork
10. isthmus

Skills

1. San José
2. New Orleans
3. October
4. New Orleans
5. February

Writing

1. An adequate response will describe at least two artifacts found in La Venta and will outline what they tell us about the Olmec. For example, the plaza contained four stone heads, which were probably statues of Olmec rulers. Carvings indicate that the Olmec had specialized workers. An excellent response will describe several artifacts and give a detailed explanation as to what the artifacts tell us about the Olmec. For example, the largest of the stone heads found in the plaza weighed 24 tons. Each has its own symbol on its helmet. Delicate objects made from jade and obsidian by specialist craftworkers were probably for religious use. The Olmec practiced polytheism and their altars indicate that they made sacrifices to their gods. The mosaic, statues and carvings of the jaguar indicate its importance in Olmec culture.

2. An adequate response will compare and contrast the Hopewell and the Adena, particularly with regard to the earthworks. For example, the two cultures inhabited the same area, but they settled there at different times. Both cultures built mounds but the Hopewell mounds were larger than those of the Adena, and shaped differently. An excellent response will provide a detailed comparison and contrast between the two cultures. For example, the Adena began to settle in the Ohio River valley around 500 B.C. and their culture had weakened by the second century A.D. The Hopewell appeared in the same area around 100 B.C. and flourished for at least 500 years. The Adena buried their dead in pits or log tombs, often including many valuable goods. The Hopewell also buried objects with people. The Adena usually buried tombs in the same place, year after year. Some built a circle of earth around a burial mound, which is thought to be of religious significance. A Hopewell mound was larger, and could contain several hundred graves.

Content and Skills

1. d
2. a
3. c
4. c
5. a
6. c
7. c
8. d
9. b
10. d

11. dharma
12. totem
13. dynasty
14. provinces
15. mosaic
16. steppes
17. isthmus
18. levees
19. karma
20. citadel

Writing

1. An adequate response will describe how the origins of Buddhism lay in the experiences of a prince of a kingdom near the Himalayas. This prince, Siddhartha Guatama, embarked on a series of travels seeking wisdom and the meaning of life. After traveling for a number of years, Siddhartha achieved an understanding of the meaning of life, earning the title Buddha. His teachings incorporated some elements of Hinduism but not others. After Buddha's death, his teaching spread from northern India to the south and east, becoming a strong force throughout Asia. Today, there are more than 330 million Buddhists. An excellent response will add such details as the title Buddha meaning "Awakened One." It will also give details about Buddhist teachings, noting its emphasis on ending suffering. It may also describe how different Buddhist schools of thought have developed over the years.

2. An adequate response will identify Mohenjo-Daro as a leading city in the ancient Indus Valley civilization. It will use the information in the chart as a starting point in describing this civilization. The existence of a large citadel and the careful planning with which the city was built indicate that the society had a strong government. The grain warehouse indicates that farming was successful, with farmers being able to grow surplus food. The artifacts that have been found indicate a society which had highly skilled craftworkers. An excellent response will mention other aspects of Mohenjo-Daro, such as the existence of a large "city-hall" and a sewer system, which also indicate the strength of the government of the society.

CHAPTER 11

Content

1. a
2. b
3. d
4. b
5. a

6. Deborah
7. Solomon
8. Moses
9. David
10. Abraham

Skills

1. the destruction of Jericho
2. sometimes it is tedious, but sometimes it can be very exciting
3. that it was caused by an earthquake followed by a fire and that it happened very quickly
4. "I'm convinced," "must have been," "seems to have been," "nor have we found," and "must have happened"
5. that it is very exciting

Writing

1. An adequate response will include one similarity and one difference between the reigns of David and Solomon. A similarity is that both were wise leaders who achieved great things. A difference is that David reigned during a time of war, and Solomon reigned during a time of peace and prosperity. An excellent response will provide more details. For example, David conquered the Philistines and people in lands bordering Israel. He also conquered Jerusalem and united the Hebrews. During Solomon's reign, Israel was a nation of wealth and splendor. The Torah was written down at this time. Like David, Solomon taxed the people, but unlike them, he forced the people of Northern Canaan to work, and refused to let them hold government positions. This caused unrest in the people of Northern Canaan, which led to the division of the nation which David had united.

2. An adequate response will describe the basic geography of ancient Canaan; for example, that it was varied, and the north was more suited to human settlement than the south. It will explain that people settled in the fertile areas of ancient Canaan. An excellent response will provide more details. For example; farmers settled around natural springs and oases, the land by the Mediterranean was fertile and provided grain for food. Because these fertile areas where people settled were scattered, Canaan was a land of small, independent city-states. Canaan's central location was good for trade, but it also made people there vulnerable to attack from their neighbors.

CHAPTER 12

Content

1. b
2. c
3. a
4. a
5. d

6. Sparta
7. Carthage
8. Athens
9. Strait of Gibraltar
10. Mount Olympus

Skills

1. It shows places at a time in the past.
2. It shows what symbol is used to represent a city-state.
3. Lindus
4. about 80 miles
5. The Ionian Sea

Writing

1. An adequate response will say that by 600 B.C., Athens had an oligarchy. Before that it had a monarchy, like other Greek city-states, and later, a democracy. In all the governments of ancient Greece, the leaders had to be citizens of the polis. An excellent response will explain what each type of government was and how Athens became a democracy. An oligarchy is when the richest and most powerful citizens controlled decision making. A monarchy is rule by one. The poorer citizens of Athens demanded more power at the time of Athens' oligarchy, and forced the nobles into sharing power, hence Athens became a democracy.

2. An adequate response will state that when Assyria was on the rise, the Phoenicians had begun to set up colonies around the Mediterranean, far away from their homeland. The response will also outline the threat from Assyria and Babylonia, which influenced the Phoenicians' westward expansion. An excellent response will provide more detail. For example, there were even a few Phoenician colonies beyond the Strait of Gibraltar. The colonies provided valuable resources, shipped grain to cities back home, and acted as rest stops or escape routes for troubles at home. Carthage became important after the fall of Tyre and ruled trade between the eastern and western Mediterranean.

CHAPTER 13

Content

1. a	6. c
2. d	7. e
3. c	8. b
4. b	9. d
5. d	10. a

Skills

1. Bias is a slanted, or strongly one-sided presentation of information.
2. Using loaded words such as "our pride, our noblest symbol of excellence" or "the finest of Greek creation."
3. Possible answer: Yes; the speaker uses loaded words and implies that keeping the Elgin marbles in the British Museum is not logical.
4. The writer is Greek and wants the Elgin marbles returned to Greece.
5. to determine the accuracy of information

Writing

1. An adequate response will identify Pericles as an important ruler of Athens during its Golden Age. It will note that Pericles helped change the face of the city of Athens by having experts design expensive, beautiful buildings and temples, and that he helped expand democracy in Athens by allowing poor or working citizens more of a role in government. An excellent response will provide more detail; for example, the statues and buildings built during Pericles' time portrayed ordinary citizens, which broke with Greek tradition. The response will define what a jury is and point out that working citizens were allowed to serve on a jury. Pericles was also responsible for a bill that said citizens were to be paid when serving on a jury or in a government job.

2. An adequate response will summarize the Peloponnesian War as a conflict between Sparta and its allies on the Peloponnesian peninsula and Athens and its allies. The cause of the war was Sparta's worry that Athens was becoming too powerful. The war lasted nearly 30 years, with Sparta winning land battles and Athens winning those at sea. An excellent response will provide more detail, such as the fact that the Athenians were able to hold out inside the city walls for a long time, in spite of an outbreak of disease, of which Pericles was one of the victims. Athens surrendered after Sparta cut off the grain supply from the Black Sea, causing the Athenians to starve. The effects of the war were that no city-state was able to maintain control of Greece for any length of time after Sparta's victory. This meant that Greece was vulnerable to attack from the north.

Content and Skills

1. a
2. b
3. a
4. a
5. c
6. b
7. c
8. a
9. b
10. d

11. monotheism
12. oligarchy
13. proverb
14. polis
15. jury
16. tragedy
17. covenant
18. prophet
19. helot
20. oasis

Writing

1 An adequate response will describe how interest in the arts and philosophy increased during Athens' Golden Age. Theater, literature, and music flourished, and magnificent buildings were built. New teachers taught debating and public speaking. An excellent response will provide more information, for example, describing the Parthenon which portrayed ordinary citizens as well as gods and goddesses. Comedy and tragedy were two popular forms of drama. The response will also define philosophy and note that some of the questions philosophers asked involved what it meant to be a good citizen and what makes something beautiful.

2. An adequate response will describe the basics of Hebrew law, noting that they were similar to the laws that were common in Babylonia, like the Code of Hammurabi. These laws, like those of the Hebrews, forbade stealing and hurting others. The most important difference was that the Hebrews worshipped one God. An excellent response will elaborate on these points; the Hebrew's monotheism was central to their belief. The Ten Commandments, given by God to Moses on Mount Sinai, are the central part of Jewish religion and teachings. The response will also describe the Torah. The Torah consists of five books, which are the first books of the Bible. This is the basis of life and faith for Jews; for example, it instructs people to remember the Sabbath, a day of rest, prayer and study. It contains guidance on day to day living, such as rules about what Jews could and could not eat. Some of its teachings are in the form of stories, such as the one concerning Daniel in the lions' den.

CHAPTER 14

Content

1. d
2. c
3. a
4. c
5. b

6. patricians
7. tribunes
8. republic
9. Senate
10. consuls

Skills

1. in the Alps, or in the north
2. 0 ft.–700 ft.
3. about 1,500 ft.–7,000 ft.
4. It shows differences in the height of land areas.
5. It could show relative height better than an elevation map can.

Writing

1. An adequate response will give a basic description of the geography of Italy. Examples: The Italian peninsula is part of the European continent, jutting out into the Mediterranean sea. The Alps are a mountain range on the northern border and the Apennine mountain range is situated down the center of the peninsula. An excellent response will provide more detail. For example, the Alps are Europe's highest mountain range and they wall off Italy from the rest of Europe. The Apennines make it difficult to travel across the peninsula and are lacking in rich soil, making farming difficult there. Italy has several fertile plains, one of which is Latium. The Tiber river runs through the center of this plain.

2. An adequate response will note that Rome's system of government was a republic in which citizens elected representatives to act for them. It will describe the three branches of Roman government: the Senate, the tribunes and the consul. It will also mention the citizen assembly. An excellent response will go on to point out that not all of Rome's inhabitants had an equal say in the government. Women, for example, were not citizens, and the votes of the people were not equal. It will point out that the citizen assembly had the power to veto the consul's actions and note that both patricians and plebeians had a role in Rome's government. It was the plebeian's protest against unwritten laws that led to the Twelve Tables.

CHAPTER 15

Content

1. a
2. c
3. c
4. d
5. d

6. false
7. false
8. true
9. true
10. true

Skills

1. Determine if you can trust its accuracy.
2. Yes; Tacitus was a Roman historian.
3. Possible answer: Yes; Tacitus, as a historian, has first-hand experience and he bases his writing on fact not opinion.
4. Neither; he does not take sides, saying the source of the fire is "uncertain."
5. More; it shows he knows what he's talking about.

Writing

1. An adequate response will state that the Pax Romana was a long period of peace that began under the emperor Augustus in 27 B.C. It will give several examples of changes, such as the building of roads, buildings and water systems, and the development of a strong central government. An excellent response will give detailed examples of changes that took place. For example, during the 200 years of the Pax Romana, more than 50,000 miles of roads criss-crossed the Roman empire. The government raised money through taxes. Engineers built bridges, aqueducts and many beautiful buildings and temples, such as the Colosseum. The army protected citizens and there was a mail service in the empire. It was a time of prosperous travel and trade.

2. An adequate response will state that the Romans treated the Christians badly before Constantine and were protected after his reign. Christians would not worship Roman gods and were persecuted for this, often being tortured and killed. Constantine, during his reign, protected Christianity. An excellent response will explain that Constantine's dream before his battle led him to have his soldiers mark crosses on their shields; they won the battle. Because of this, Constantine granted freedom to Christians and became the first European ruler to protect Christianity. In time, Christianity became the first official religion of the Roman empire.

UNIT 6

Content and Skills

1. c
2. a
3. a
4. b
5. b
6. d
7. a
8. c
9. b
10. c

11. Augustus
12. Forum
13. Diocletian
14. Gaul
15. Carthage
16. Paul
17. Latium
18. Hannibal
19. Nazareth
20. Colosseum

Writing

1. An adequate response will mention two legacies or achievements of Roman civilization. Example: Romans developed the republican form of government, in which citizens elect government leaders to represent them. The Romans were also the first to make cement. An excellent response will mention two or more legacies and explain why each is still important today. Examples: The republican form of government is widely used today, including in the United States. We still use cement in the construction of modern buildings and roads. Other legacies include the Roman alphabet and Latin-based languages, aqueducts to bring water to cities, a mail system, the use of arches in buildings, and an advanced road system.

2. An adequate response will give persuasive reasons for stating that Romans were better off during the years of the republic or during the Pax Romana. Example: Romans were better off during the Pax Romana than during the years of the republic. Although citizens were no longer able to participate in government, their emperors helped to improve living conditions by building new roads, water systems, and public buildings. They also maintained strong armies for protection. An excellent response will explain in more detail why Romans were better off in one period than in the other.

Part 3

Chapter and Unit Tests

CONTENT

Fill in the circle before the correct answer.

1. Culture is a people's _____.
   - ⓐ way of life
   - ⓑ technology
   - ⓒ region
   - ⓓ geography

2. A *climate region* is marked by similarities in _____.
   - ⓐ customs
   - ⓑ landforms
   - ⓒ longitude
   - ⓓ weather

3. What is one thing that helps make up a cultural region?
   - ⓐ physical boundaries
   - ⓒ weather
   - ⓑ language
   - ⓓ economy

4. Which fact about the boy Azeez shows what is meant by a *custom*?
   - ⓐ He lives in a city.
   - ⓒ He never eats meat.
   - ⓑ He is Indian.
   - ⓓ He has a brother.

5. Which example explains why people in early times settled in a region?
   - ⓐ They settled in areas that had a cold climate.
   - ⓑ They moved to places that were far away from the sea.
   - ⓒ They chose places they could defend against attack.
   - ⓓ They chose to settle away from land and water routes.

Write the word or phrase from the box that best answers each question.

representative democracy	physical region	English
political region	cultural value	

6. What kind of region is the Mississippi River valley? _____

7. In 1990, when East and West Germany joined to become the Federal Republic of Germany, what type of region was changed? _____

8. Most Hindus believe that all living things have souls. This is an example of a _____.

9. Britain took over India's government in 1858, and as a result, many Indians today still speak _____.

10. What kind of government does India have? _____

SKILLS

Latitude and longitude are sometimes used to set boundaries between countries, states, and other areas. Use the map below to answer the questions. Write your answers on the lines.

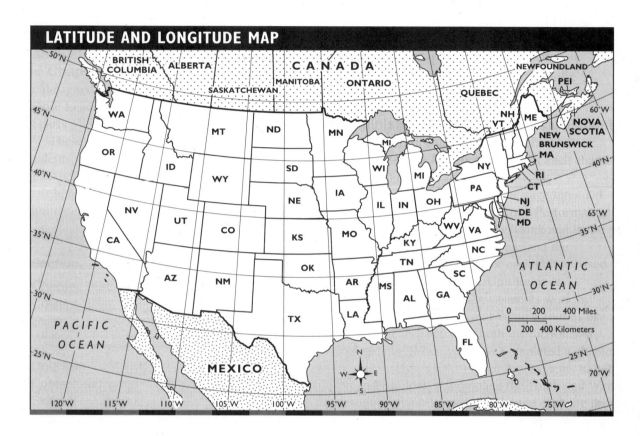

LATITUDE AND LONGITUDE MAP

1. The southwestern corner of Tennessee is located at _____.

2. 110°W marks the boundary between which two Canadian provinces?

   _____

3. The point 40°N, 100°W lies on the boundary between which two states?

   _____

4. The southernmost point in the continental United States shown on this map lies in which state and at about what latitude and longitude?

   _____

5. Which three states meet at about 42°N, 120°W?

   _____

WRITING

Write a short paragraph to answer each question. If you need more room, continue writing on the back of this page.

1. Use the map below to describe the continent of Australia in terms of climate regions.

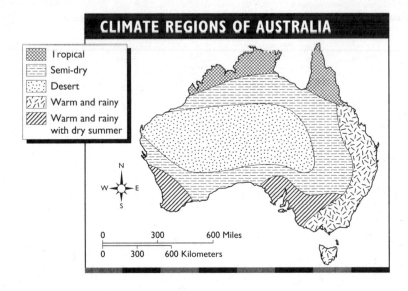

_____

_____

_____

_____

_____

_____

2. What is the difference between customs and culture? Give examples of each in your answer.

_____

_____

_____

_____

_____

_____

CONTENT

Fill in the circle before the correct answer.

1. Which is a *primary source* for learning about pioneer life?
   - (a) a history textbook
   - (c) a book based on pioneers' stories
   - (b) an encyclopedia article
   - (d) a letter by a pioneer woman

2. What is one problem faced by people who study ancient history?
   - (a) Many important sources have been destroyed or lost.
   - (b) There are no written records from ancient times.
   - (c) Most of the sources are primary sources.
   - (d) The original purpose of most artifacts is unknown.

3. What information about an archaeological sample can be obtained by using X-rays?
   - (a) how old it is
   - (c) what it is made of
   - (b) how quickly it decayed
   - (d) what climate it is from

4. What made the "Iceman" discovery so interesting to archaeologists?
   - (a) The man had died in an accident.
   - (b) The man's clothing and possessions were preserved with him.
   - (c) The body was the first ever found in the Alps.
   - (d) The man's ax was made of copper and chipped stone.

5. How did archaeologists figure out what the Iceman's net was used for?
   - (a) They found prehistoric pictures of people using that kind of net.
   - (b) They studied the objects discovered near it.
   - (c) They compared it to a kind of net still in use in the region today.
   - (d) They tried fishing and catching birds with it.

Write the letter of the definition that best fits each term.

6. _____ historian

7. _____ oral tradition

8. _____ artifact

9. _____ archaeology

10. _____ prehistory

a. the time before writing was developed

b. an object made by someone in the past

c. the practice of passing on history from one person to another by word of mouth

d. a person who studies the past

e. the study of the remains of past cultures

Name: Date:

SKILLS

Read the paragraphs. Then answer the questions below.

Philip was helping his father dig a large hole in their backyard when he found it: a small silver coin that looked as if it were very old.

"I can't read the date," Philip said as he showed the coin to his father.

"I can't either, but it doesn't look as if it's from this century. Let's see if we can find some more." By the end of the afternoon, Philip and his father had found 12 old coins, all of them without dates.

"I wonder how they got here," Philip's mother said as the family examined the coins after dinner. Philip smiled at her. "I think I might know a way we can find out," he said.

Philip had been working at the public library over the summer. Although he had never been inside the library's map room, he knew there were maps of the town going back 200 years. He hoped he could find what building had once stood where his parent's house was now located.

Philip was disappointed at first. Since none of the landmarks in his neighborhood were on the old maps, he had trouble locating the area where his house was now. Then he remembered that the park across the street from his home dated back to the Civil War. He finally found what he was looking for.

"Mom! Dad!" Philip shouted as he ran in the back door. "You're never going to believe this! There used to be a *bank* on this corner!"

1. What problem did Philip need to solve?

_____

2. What information did Philip collect to help him try and solve the problem?

_____

3. What steps did Philip take to evaluate the information he had collected?

_____

4. What kind of solution did Philip find for the problem?

_____

5. Do you think Philip arrived at a good solution? Why or why not?

_____

_____

_____

WRITING

Read the selection. Then write a short paragraph to answer each question. If you need more room, continue writing on the back of this page.

All his life, Thomas Obed Madden, Jr. heard stories about his family. Central to these stories, was his great-great-grandmother, Sally Madden. Sally worked very hard at keeping the family together during a time when many African American families were separated. One of her ten children, Willis, inherited Sally's determination and enterprising nature. He became a shrewd businessman before the Civil War.

Fascinated by these family legends, Madden wanted to know more about his family's heritage. His search led him to his great-grandfather's trunk, which sat forgotten for nearly a century. It contained many documents, including photographs, freedom papers, letters, birth certificates, and deeds of land. This documentation confirmed that the stories he was told over the years were true!

He continued his investigation by using census reports, more family documents and interviews. He learned all about Sally Madden. Because her mother was an Irish immigrant, Sally was born free. However, since her father was an African American slave, the law forced her to be an indentured servant to Colonel James Madison's family in 1758. T.O. Madden, Jr. combined all these sources to write a book entitled *We Were Always Free*. The book dates back two hundred years and tells a wonderful American story about the Madden family.

1. Describe the sources T.O. Madden, Jr. used in learning about his family's history. Tell what kind of source each one was and how it helped him.

_____

_____

_____

_____

2. Suppose that 1,000 years from now, archaeologists discover a copy of *We Were Always Free*. Do you think it would be a good source of information about American history? Tell why or why not.

_____

_____

_____

_____

CONTENT AND SKILLS

Fill in the circle before the correct answer.

1. To understand Earth better, geographers divide it into different types of _____.
   - (a) landforms
   - (b) regions
   - (c) customs
   - (d) peoples

2. A region is _____.
   - (a) an area with common features
   - (b) an early harvest
   - (c) a large continent
   - (d) an ancient settlement

3. Contact between two cultures that often leads to cultural change is called _____.
   - (a) cultural interaction
   - (b) oral history
   - (c) cultural region
   - (d) values

4. The work of historians is similar to that of detectives because they both _____.
   - (a) display artifacts in museums
   - (b) create primary sources
   - (c) use clues to solve mysteries
   - (d) study ancient cultures

5. Ancient Athens was a good area for settlement because _____.
   - (a) it was a famous city
   - (b) it had a cool climate
   - (c) it was many miles from the sea
   - (d) it was on a plain good for farming

6. Why did archaeologists working at the Iceman site melt the snow and filter the water?
   - (a) They wanted to see if the water was clean.
   - (b) They did not want to lose any evidence.
   - (c) They needed drinking water.
   - (d) They wanted to clean the Iceman.

7. Bits of sulfur and iron, which are used to make matches, were found in a piece of fungus carried by the Iceman. This suggests that the Iceman _____.
   - (a) was a miner
   - (b) invented matches
   - (c) traded with other people
   - (d) knew how to make fire

8. What important development began in the New Stone Age?
   - (a) agriculture
   - (b) cave painting
   - (c) stone tools
   - (d) fire

9. All cultures are made up of many different _____.
   - (a) sources
   - (b) customs
   - (c) regions
   - (d) languages

10. You can learn about the culture of a country by studying _____.
    - (a) oral history
    - (b) maps
    - (c) diaries
    - (d) its past

CONTENT AND SKILLS

Suppose that you are studying the history of your community. Match the type of source to each example of information by writing the letter on the line.

11. _____ primary source

12. _____ secondary source

13. _____ oral tradition

14. _____ artifact

a. a story of long ago told by a resident of the area

b. a diary written by one of the founders of the community

c. an object from the past found at a construction site

d. a TV documentary about people who lived in the area

Use the map to answer questions 15–17.

15. What type of region does this map illustrate?

   _____

16. What is the location (longitude and latitude) of Caracas?

   _____

17. What kind of landform would you find in Bogotá?

   _____

Write the term that best fits each description on the left.

18. the study of past cultures _____   **viewpoint**

19. a position from which objects are viewed and judged _____   **prehistory**

20. the time before writing was developed _____   **archaeology**

WRITING

Write a short paragraph to answer each question. If you need more room, continue writing on the back of this page.

1. Cari found the artifacts below in her uncle's attic. Describe the steps Cari might take to find out how old the artifacts are.

_____

_____

_____

_____

_____

2. Suppose that you have to make a decision about whether or not to spend next summer working at an archaeological dig. Describe the steps you would take to make the decision.

_____

_____

_____

_____

_____

_____

CONTENT

Fill in the circle before the correct answer.

1. Remains or imprints of ancient life preserved in Earth's crust are called _____.
   - (a) fossils
   - (b) theories
   - (c) descendants
   - (d) ancestors

2. Scientists believe that the first human ancestors appeared in _____.
   - (a) Hadar
   - (b) The Great Rift Valley
   - (c) the Neander Valley
   - (d) Beringia

3. Tools found near the remains of *Homo habilis* were made of _____.
   - (a) metal
   - (b) bone
   - (c) wood
   - (d) stone

4. What conclusion have scientists drawn about the people of Border Cave in South Africa?
   - (a) They farmed the land.
   - (b) They made and used money.
   - (c) They had religious beliefs.
   - (d) They had a system of writing.

5. Scientists believe that the Beringia land bridge once connected the Americas to _____.
   - (a) Europe
   - (b) Asia
   - (c) Africa
   - (d) Antarctica

Match each term with the descripton that goes with it.

6. _____ These human ancestors were short and squat and had large brains.

7. _____ These first modern humans decorated caves with art.

8. _____ These early human ancestors were named by Louis and Mary Leakey.

9. _____ These early humans probably traveled many miles to hunt eland.

10. _____ These early Americans made tools in the same way as some early Europeans.

a. The people of Border Cave

b. Neanderthals

c. *Australopithecus*

d. the Clovis people

e. Cro-Magnons

SKILLS

Use the time line below to answer the questions.

HUMAN ANCESTORS

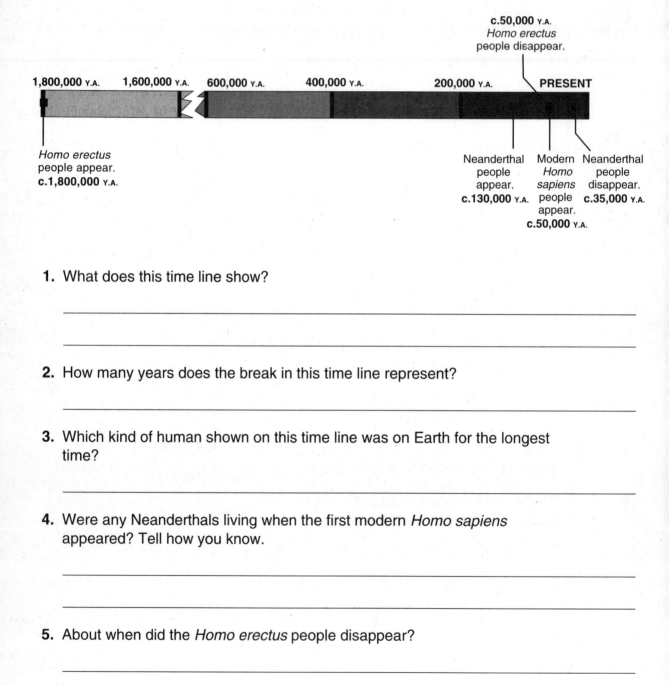

1. What does this time line show?

   _____

   _____

2. How many years does the break in this time line represent?

   _____

3. Which kind of human shown on this time line was on Earth for the longest time?

   _____

4. Were any Neanderthals living when the first modern *Homo sapiens* appeared? Tell how you know.

   _____

   _____

5. About when did the *Homo erectus* people disappear?

   _____

WRITING

Write a short paragraph to answer each question. If you need more room, continue writing on the back of this page.

1. This map shows where fossil remains of *Homo habilis* and *Homo erectus* were found in Africa, Asia, and Europe. What can you tell about these ancestors from the map?

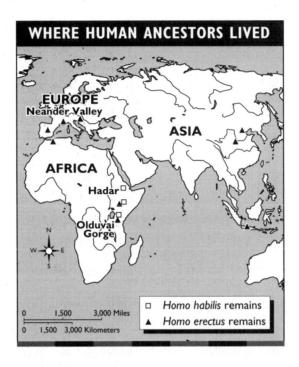

WHERE HUMAN ANCESTORS LIVED

EUROPE
Neander Valley
ASIA
AFRICA
Hadar
Olduvai Gorge

0   1,500   3,000 Miles
0   1,500   3,000 Kilometers

□ *Homo habilis* remains
▲ *Homo erectus* remains

_____

_____

_____

_____

2. Imagine that you are an archaeologist digging for evidence of early humans. In the area where you are working, you have uncovered a stone tool shaped like an ax blade, several stone arrowheads, and a necklace made from animal teeth and bones. However, you have not found any human skeleton remains. Based on this evidence, what can you tell about the people who made these objects?

_____

_____

_____

_____

CONTENT

Fill in the circle before the correct answer.

1. During the New Stone Age, what did people begin to do for the first time?
   - (a) make weapons for hunting
   - (b) migrate from place to place
   - (c) experiment with agriculture
   - (d) use fire for cooking and heat

2. The people of Catal Huyuk built homes made mainly of _____.
   - (a) brick
   - (b) timber
   - (c) hides
   - (d) stone

3. What happened in Catal Huyuk because there was a food surplus?
   - (a) Farmers became the wealthiest and most important citizens.
   - (b) Farmers could exchange food for other products.
   - (c) Farmers stopped taming and breeding animals.
   - (d) Most people did not have to work for a living.

4. Catal Huyuk attracted many visitors who mostly wanted to _____.
   - (a) teach the people new skills
   - (b) learn how the government worked
   - (c) see the temples and paintings
   - (d) trade for crafts and other goods

5. What problem was often caused by slash-and-burn farming?
   - (a) Fertile topsoil washed away.
   - (b) Crops were damaged by pests.
   - (c) Water supplies dried up.
   - (d) Weeds crowded out crops.

Read each sentence. Write the term from the box that best matches the idea expressed in the sentence.

civilization	revolution	specialization	agriculture	terraces

6. To feed themselves, people of Catal Huyuk planted wheat and barley.   _____

7. In Catal Huyuk goods such as flour, pots, and tools were made by different workers.   _____

8. The culture of Catal Huyuk included systems of religion, learning, and government.   _____

9. As people learned more about farming, they developed ways to plant crops on hillsides.   _____

10. The switch from hunting and gathering to farming spread around the world and brought great and lasting effects.   _____

SKILLS

For each question, circle the letter of the conclusion that can be made based on the information given.

1. When archaeologists found the ruins of Catal Huyuk, it was not just a lucky accident. There was good reason to think ancient farmers might have settled in southern Turkey. It is an area with fertile soil and abundant grasslands for grazing herds.

   (a) Archaeologists believed southern Turkey was a good place to look for the remains of an ancient farming community.

   (b) Archaeologists searched many areas without any luck before they finally found the ruins of Catal Huyuk.

2. It is not known for sure when Catal Huyuk was first settled. Archaeologists have uncovered some remains that are 8,500 years old. But the first houses built in Catal Huyuk, located in the bottom layers of the site, may be even older than that.

   (a) Archaeologists are not interested in uncovering the bottom layers of Catal Huyuk.

   (b) The earliest houses built in Catal Huyuk have not been uncovered and studied yet.

3. Catal Huyuk had buildings designed for religious activities. These buildings were often decorated with images of animals. For example, a deer hunt was drawn on the wall of one shrine.

   (a) Animals played an important role in the religious beliefs of the Catal Huyuk people.

   (b) Highly skilled artists decorated the religious buildings of Catal Huyuk.

4. A variety of expertly crafted objects have been found at Catal Huyuk. These include metal tools, wooden caskets, and delicate pottery. Of course, few people would have the skill to make all these objects for themselves.

   (a) Most people in Catal Huyuk had collections of beautiful objects.

   (b) In Catal Huyuk, people specialized in different crafts and occupations.

5. Obsidian, a sharp glass found in volcanic rock, was plentiful near Catal Huyuk. Outsiders traveled to the city to trade for it. They used it to make sharp-edged tools and weapons.

   (a) Outsiders thought of the people of Catal Huyuk as their enemies.

   (b) A volcano was located near Catal Huyuk.

SKILLS

Use the cartogram below to answer the questions.

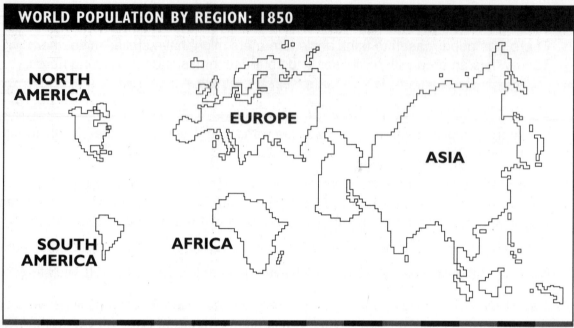

WORLD POPULATION BY REGION: 1850

NORTH AMERICA

EUROPE

ASIA

SOUTH AMERICA

AFRICA

Source: *World Almanac*, 1996.

6. What is the purpose of this cartogram?

_____

7. How is this cartogram different from a physical map of the world?

_____

8. What do you know about Asia from looking at this cartogram?

_____

9. What comparison between Europe and North America can you make using this cartogram?

_____

10. Which region had the fewest people in 1850? Tell how you know.

_____

WRITING

Write a short paragraph to answer each question. If you need more room, continue writing on the back of this page.

1. This map shows areas of the Middle East where wheat and barley once grew wild. Find Catal Huyuk on the map. Based on its location, what conclusions can you draw about how and why the city of Catal Huyuk came to exist?

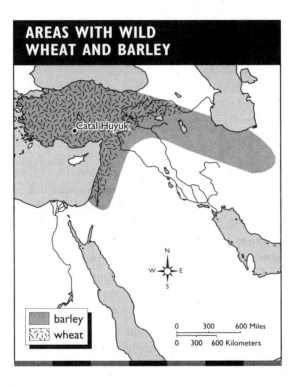

_____

_____

_____

_____

2. Imagine that you belong to a group of New Stone Age hunter-gatherers. One day your group comes upon Catal Huyuk. After observing the way the people of Catal Huyuk live, does your group decide to create a permanent settlement, or continue hunting and gathering? Give reasons for your decision.

_____

_____

_____

_____

CONTENT AND SKILLS

Fill in the circle before the correct answer.

1. According to most scientists, the first human ancestors appeared on Earth about how many years ago?

   ⓐ 5 million   ⓑ 2.5 million   ⓒ 500,000   ⓓ 250,000

2. Which human ancestor was the first to make tools?

   ⓐ *Autralopithecus*   ⓒ *Homo erectus*

   ⓑ *Homo habilis*   ⓓ *Homo sapiens*

3. Learning to control fire was important because it allowed people to _____.

   ⓐ explore and survive in cold climates   ⓒ hunt animals for food

   ⓑ make homes in caves   ⓓ develop skills as craftspeople

4. What did scientists conclude about Neanderthals who buried their dead?

   ⓐ They suffered from many diseases.   ⓒ They had developed religious beliefs.

   ⓑ They lived in one place for life.   ⓓ They did not experience emotions.

5. The Cro-Magnon people were the first humans to _____.

   ⓐ build permanent homes   ⓒ domesticate wild animals

   ⓑ use language   ⓓ create art

6. Scientists believe that Beringia was _____.

   ⓐ a migration route   ⓒ the home of the first farmers

   ⓑ the location of an early city   ⓓ the home of the first human ancestors

7. A cartogram of different regions is used mainly to _____.

   ⓐ display many different facts   ⓒ compare information about the regions

   ⓑ show physical land features   ⓓ show exact size of different countries

8. By using agriculture, people could live together without having to _____.

   ⓐ cooperate to solve problems   ⓒ develop specialized jobs

   ⓑ use technology   ⓓ move about to find food

9. The ruins of Catal Huyuk are located in what present-day country?

   ⓐ South Africa   ⓑ Germany   ⓒ Turkey   ⓓ China

10. Farmers turned to slash-and-burn agriculture in order to _____.

    ⓐ prevent fertile soil from eroding   ⓒ create grazing land for animals

    ⓑ clear forests to make new farmland   ⓓ grow crops on hillsides

CONTENT AND SKILLS

Use the time line to answer the questions.

EARLY BREAKTHROUGHS IN FARMING

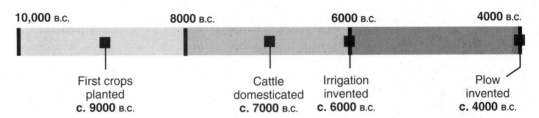

11. How many years does this time line cover? _____

12. Which came first, the invention of irrigation or
    the domestication of cattle? _____

13. About how many years passed between the time
    the first crops were planted and irrigation was
    invented? _____

14. Is 6000 B.C. the exact year in which irrigation was invented? Explain.

    _____

15. Did the first farmers use plows to plant their crops? Tell how you know.

    _____

    _____

Write the term from the box that completes each sentence.

| Border Cave   specialization   Catal Huyuk   revolution   theory |

16. Archaeologists have gathered much evidence to support the _____
    that the first humans appeared in Africa.

17. Like other people of the Paleolithic era, the people of _____ survived
    by hunting wild animals and gathering fruits, roots, and vegetables.

18. The beginnings of agriculture brought about a _____ in the way
    people lived.

19. In settlements such as _____, a small number of farmers were able to
    raise enough food to feed everyone.

20. A surplus of food led to _____ since many people could learn
    particular jobs and skills instead of looking for food themselves.

WRITING

Write a short paragraph to answer each question. If you need more room, continue writing on the back of this page.

1. Explain one way in which the physical environment influenced the way people lived during the Old Stone Age, and explain how these people began to gain control over their environment.

_____

_____

_____

_____

2. Look at this sketch of an archaeological site. What conclusions can you make about when this settlement was built, the people who lived here, and their way of life?

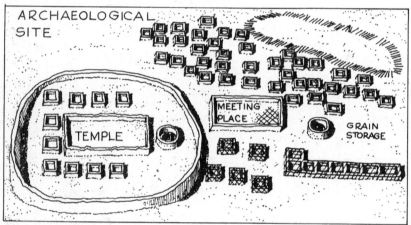

_____

_____

_____

_____

CONTENT

Fill in the circle before the correct answer.

1. In ancient Sumer each city-state had a ziggurat where people went to _____.
   - ⓐ learn to write cuneiform
   - ⓑ worship a special god or goddess
   - ⓒ trade with people from other cities
   - ⓓ buy clothes and food

2. What factor made it especially difficult to farm in southern Mesopotamia?
   - ⓐ unskilled laborers
   - ⓑ droughts and irregular floods
   - ⓒ not enough sunshine
   - ⓓ rocky, infertile soil

3. The Code of Hammurabi was a _____.
   - ⓐ set of laws
   - ⓑ form of writing
   - ⓒ type of alphabet
   - ⓓ system of taxes

4. Trained scribes were important in ancient Sumer because _____.
   - ⓐ they helped irrigate crops
   - ⓑ they could write fast
   - ⓒ they kept records
   - ⓓ they taught people to write

5. Nineveh was important because it became the _____.
   - ⓐ capital city of Assyria
   - ⓑ first city-state in Sumer
   - ⓒ first city with hanging gardens
   - ⓓ birthplace of cuneiform writing

Read each sentence and write the name from the box of the person it describes.

Gilgamesh	Sargon	Hammurabi	Enheduana	Nebuchadnezzar

6. This king of Babylon dammed parts of the Euphrates River and attacked the Sumerians. _____

7. Under this king, Babylon became one of the ancient world's largest cities. _____

8. He was an important hero to the Sumerians. _____

9. This king of Kish used cuneiform to expand his empire and unite the other city-states. _____

10. This priestess wrote a poem praising Sumer's gods and goddesses when the city-states were united under one ruler. _____

SKILLS

Read the passage. Then complete the chart below by writing in the missing causes and effects.

     The Sumerians lived in an environment with limited resources. Southern Mesopotamia was very hot and dry, receiving hardly any rain each year. Trees cannot grow in such a place. Even rocks were hard to find. The Sumerians needed to find another material from which to build shelter. Fortunately, sunshine and clay were plentiful. As a result, the Sumerians packed moist clay into molds and left it to dry in the sun. Since the flat bricks could then be stacked, they were used to form the walls of buildings.

     Because the Sumerians were not happy with the way the sun-dried bricks eventually crumbled, they found a better way to work with the clay. They found out that if they baked the bricks, they were harder and lasted longer. Using a natural material called asphalt to join the bricks, they could make a long-lasting wall. The Sumerians built massive and long-lasting ziggurats, parts of which have survived four thousand years. As a result, archaeologists can study these remains to learn about the Sumerians.

CAUSES	EFFECTS
1.	1. The Sumerians made buildings out of clay.
2. The Sumerians made flat bricks that could be stacked.	2.
3.	3. The Sumerians experimented with baked bricks.
4. The Sumerians used asphalt to join the bricks.	4.
5.	5. Archaeologists can learn about the Sumerians from their remains.

WRITING

Write a short paragraph to answer each question. If you need more room, continue writing on the back of this page.

1. Describe the contributions of ancient Mesopotamian culture to our world today.

_____

_____

_____

_____

_____

2. Much of Mesopotamia is now called Iraq. Today most of Iraq's people live in cities, some live in villages, and a few travel with their herds of animals (mostly sheep). Look at the map of Iraq. Based on what you have learned about farming and the development of cities, where would you expect most of the people of Iraq to live? Tell why.

_____

_____

_____

_____

_____

CONTENT

Fill in the circle before the correct answer.

1. Hieroglyphics helped Egyptian scribes keep records of _____.

   (a) history   (b) speeches   (c) flooding   (d) taxes

2. Egyptian farmers used irrigation to _____.

   (a) water their crops   (c) control flood waters

   (b) make the soil more fertile (d) travel among villages

3. In Egypt's Old Kingdom what did craftworkers and artists receive in return for the objects they made for the pharaohs?

   (a) land   (c) money

   (b) clothes and food   (d) golden bowls and stone statues

4. The Middle Kingdom is best described as a time when Egypt _____.

   (a) first developed a written language

   (b) began to use irrigation techniques

   (c) increased contact with other cultures

   (d) became a wealthy empire

5. In ancient Egypt most of the land and farms were owned by _____.

   (a) hard-working farmers   (c) Nubians and Syrians

   (b) skilled craftworkers   (d) government leaders, army officials or scribes

Write the letter of the description that best fits each pharaoh.

6. _____ Hatshepsut

7. _____ Menes

8. _____ Ahmose

9. _____ Khufu

10. _____ Tutankhamun

a. ordered the construction of the Great Pyramid

b. unified Egypt by overthrowing the king of Lower Egypt and became the first pharaoh

c. organized a two-year expedition to Punt, expanding trade beyond the Egyptian empire

d. ruled as a wealthy young pharaoh from about age 9 to 19

e. studied the Hyksos and used their weapons to drive them back out of Lower Egypt

SKILLS

Use the maps to answer the questions. Write your answers on the lines.

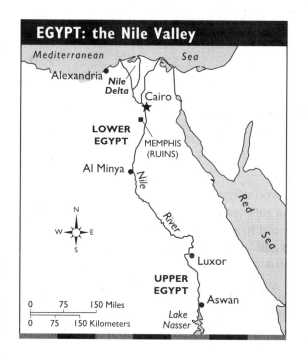

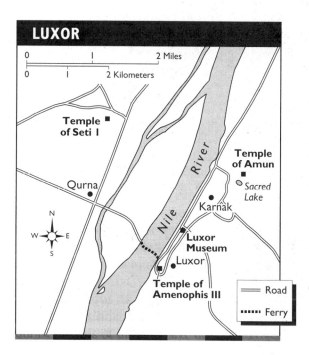

1. Approximately how far would a boat traveling from Cairo to Luxor go?

   _____

2. About how far is it from the Luxor museum to the Temple of Amun?

   _____

3. Name a city that is in Upper Egypt.

   _____

4. What is one advantage of a large-scale map over a small-scale map?

   _____

5. Which map would you use to determine the direction you would travel to go from Luxor to Alexandria?

   _____

WRITING

Write a short paragraph to answer each question. If you need more room, continue writing on the back of this page.

1. How did the development of hieroglyphics affect ancient Egyptian culture? Tell what hieroglyphs were used for and how hieroglyphics changed Egyptian culture.

_____

_____

_____

_____

_____

2. Look at the map of Egypt. Where would you expect to find the best farmland? Tell why.

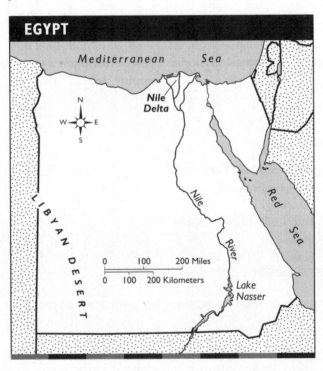

_____

_____

_____

_____

CONTENT

Fill in the circle before the correct answer.

1. Since ancient times, cattle grazing and tin mining have been important in which area?
   - (a) the Jos Plateau
   - (b) the Congo Basin
   - (c) the Ethiopian Highlands
   - (d) Mount Kilimanjaro

2. Carvings of _____ have been found in Nubian graves.
   - (a) jewelry
   - (b) cattle
   - (c) kings and queens
   - (d) weapons

3. Piye was a Kushite king who _____.
   - (a) drove the Assyrians out of Kush
   - (b) opened trade routes to Nubia
   - (c) became ruler of all Egypt
   - (d) founded the city of Kerma

4. Ancient tombs uncovered in the city of Meroë indicate that _____.
   - (a) the women of Meroë had few rights and privileges
   - (b) there was a social pyramid
   - (c) even ordinary people had many expensive possessions
   - (d) priests were the most powerful and important people in Meroë

5. What conclusion have archaeologists drawn about the Nok people?
   - (a) They depended on hunting and gathering for their food.
   - (b) They conquered several groups that lived nearby.
   - (c) They were one of the first cultures in Africa to work with iron.
   - (d) They grew cotton and wove it into cloth for clothing.

Match each term to its description by writing the letter on the line.

6. _____ smelt

7. _____ cataract

8. _____ terra cotta

9. _____ reservoir

10. _____ desert

a. a region that gets very little rainfall

b. to heat metal to remove other materials from the pure ore

c. a storage tank built to hold rain

d. a large, dangerous waterfall

e. clay pottery with a reddish-brown color

SKILLS

Read each paragraph. Decide whether the underlined sentence is a **fact**, a **reasoned judgment**, or an **opinion**. Fill in the circle before the correct answer.

1. Africa's most interesting ancient civilizations grew up along the banks of the Nile River. Both Egypt and Kush used technology and trade to grow and prosper. The Nok culture was probably not so advanced.

   (a) fact   (b) reasoned judgment   (c) opinion

2. Egyptians prized Nubian ebony, a hard black wood, because it was so scarce in Egypt. Nubian traders also offered animal skins and furs. These items were likely to have been used to make clothing and shoes.

   (a) fact   (b) reasoned judgment   (c) opinion

3. Meroë became an important iron-producing center after 600 B.C. Its large supplies of two resources made this possible. The first, of course, was iron ore. But Meroë's timber was just as important, since it fueled the furnaces used to make the iron.

   (a) fact   (b) reasoned judgment   (c) opinion

4. Archaeologists have discovered terra cotta heads and pieces of figures sculpted by people of the Nok culture. The heads of the figures are especially large, sometimes one-third the size of the body. The sculpted faces have powerful expressions, and some are even a bit frightening.

   (a) fact   (b) reasoned judgment   (c) opinion

5. At first neighboring Egypt had a strong influence on Kushite culture. But Egypt's influence probably started fading when the Kushite capital shifted south to Meroë. Soon the Kushites developed their own alphabet, art forms, and religious practices. Few traces of Egyptian culture remained.

   (a) fact   (b) reasoned judgment   (c) opinion

WRITING

Write a short paragraph to answer each question. If you need more room, continue writing on the back of this page.

1. The kingdom of Kush developed in East Africa, and the Nok culture developed in West Africa. How were these two cultures alike, and how were they different? Use the time line below to help you answer the question.

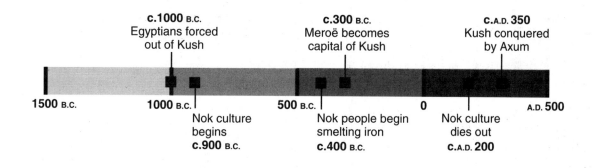

c.1000 B.C.
Egyptians forced
out of Kush

c.300 B.C.
Meroë becomes
capital of Kush

C.A.D. 350
Kush conquered
by Axum

1500 B.C.   1000 B.C.   500 B.C.   0   A.D. 500

Nok culture
begins
c.900 B.C.

Nok people begin
smelting iron
c.400 B.C.

Nok culture
dies out
C.A.D. 200

_____

_____

_____

_____

_____

_____

2. Imagine you are an archaeologist hoping to discover the remains of an ancient African civilization. At what type of site would you most likely have success? Describe the physical environment of the site you would choose.

_____

_____

_____

_____

_____

_____

_____

CONTENT AND SKILLS

Fill in the circle before the correct answer.

1. The ancient Nubian civilization developed between _____.
   - (a) 900 B.C. and A.D. 250
   - (b) 350 and 300 B.C.
   - (c) 2100 and 2000 B.C.
   - (d) 3500 and 3000 B.C.

2. Meroë was the capital city of _____.
   - (a) Egypt
   - (b) Kush
   - (c) Nubia
   - (d) Nok

3. Which leader united the Sumerian people, beginning a new era in Mesopotamia's history?
   - (a) Sargon
   - (b) Kish
   - (c) Gilgamesh
   - (d) Enheduana

4. What caused farmers in Mesopotamia to develop water control and irrigation systems?
   - (a) river silt deposits
   - (b) floods and droughts
   - (c) steady amounts of rainfall
   - (d) royal proclamations

5. How were the ancient Egyptians able to turn desert into rich farmland?
   - (a) a nearly year-long rainy season
   - (b) through the flooding of the Nile
   - (c) a drastic change in climate
   - (d) through the use of papyrus

6. The empire of Assyria had its roots in _____.
   - (a) Babylonia
   - (b) southern Egypt
   - (c) northern Mesopotamia
   - (d) southern Mesopotamia

7. During the New Kingdom, Egypt's most important trading partner was _____.
   - (a) Greece
   - (b) Kush
   - (c) Syria
   - (d) Assyria

8. A reasoned judgment _____.
   - (a) is not supported by facts
   - (b) requires definite proof
   - (c) expresses a personal belief
   - (d) has no definite proof

9. Who ordered the construction of the Great Pyramid?
   - (a) Hammurabi
   - (b) Khufu
   - (c) Menes
   - (d) Tutankhamun

10. A map scale is a unit of measure used to represent a _____ on Earth.
   - (a) height
   - (b) landmark
   - (c) location
   - (d) distance

CONTENT AND SKILLS

Write the term from the box that best fits each description.

Fertile Crescent	silt	Kerma	papyrus	Nubia
Memphis	scribes	Tigris	drought	smelt

11. The civilization that lived on the Nile south of Egypt.   _____

12. To heat metal to a high temperature to remove other materials from the pure ore.   _____

13. The region of west Asia that was home to successful farmers.   _____

14. One of the rivers that ran through the Fertile Crescent.   _____

15. Sumer's official writers.   _____

16. The capital city of ancient Egypt.   _____

17. A mixture of tiny bits of soil and rock.   _____

18. A kind of paper made from the plant of the same name.   _____

19. The original capital of the kingdom of Kush.   _____

20. A long period of dry weather.   _____

WRITING

Write a short paragraph to answer each question. If you need more room, continue writing on the back of this page.

1. Describe the relationship between Egypt, Nubia, and Kush during the New Kingdom period.

_____

_____

_____

_____

_____

2. Look at the chart below, showing the social structure of Egyptian society. Describe the role of two groups shown. What conclusions about Egyptian society can you make from the information shown in the chart?

Egyptian Social Pyramid

_____

_____

_____

_____

_____

CONTENT

Fill in the circle before the correct answer.

1. Archaeologists say that Mohenjo-Daro and Harappa might have been abandoned because of _____.

   (a) war   (b) drought   (c) invaders   (d) an earthquake

2. Much of the water that floods the Indus River comes from _____.

   (a) tides in the Arabian Sea   (c) rain falling on the Indus Plain

   (b) snow in the Himalayas   (d) streams in the Hindu Kush Mountains

3. What clue makes historians think that Mohenjo-Daro had a strong government?

   (a) sewer system design   (c) location of the city

   (b) weavers' use of cotton   (d) skill of the metalworkers

4. Why do historians know less about the Harappan civilization than they know about ancient Egyptian or Mesopotamian civilization?

   (a) People of the Harappan civilization did not trade with other cultures.

   (b) The written records have not been translated.

   (c) The Harappans did not construct large buildings.

   (d) No written records have survived the harsh climate.

5. Buddhism differs from Hinduism in that Buddhists believe _____.

   (a) all people go through a cycle of life, death, and rebirth

   (b) karma is a force based on people's behavior and affects their future lives

   (c) the most important goal is to reach peace by ending suffering

   (d) there is one powerful force that connects all life

Write the term that best completes each sentence: Vedas, caste, dharma, monk, Buddhism.

6. A special class within Hindu society is called a _____.

7. The laws and duties of members of each caste described in the Vedas are

   called _____.

8. A _____ is a man who gives up his possessions and

   devotes his life to a religious group.

9. Ancient Aryan songs that became the beginnings of Hinduism were written down in

   the _____.

10. The teachings of Siddhartha Gautama became the basis of _____.

Use the maps to answer the questions. Write your answers on the lines.

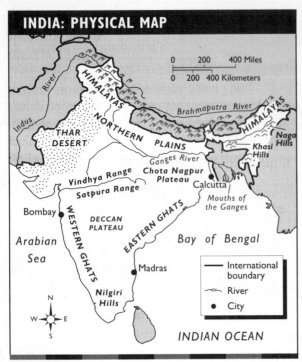
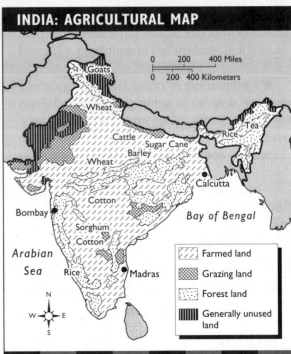

1. What is a primary use of the land along the Ganges River in northern India?

   _____

2. What kind of land is found around the Chota Nagpur Plateau?

   _____

3. In which area of India is cotton the main crop?

   _____

4. What important crops are grown on the Northern Plains?

   _____

5. Why are some land areas of northwest and far north India generally unused?

   _____

WRITING

Write a short paragraph to answer each question.. If you need more room, continue writing on the back of this page.

1. Look at the information about Pakistan's industries today. What similarities do you see between the economy of the ancient Indus Valley civilization and the economy of the country that exists in the same area today?

CHIEF INDUSTRIES IN PAKISTAN TODAY

- **Wheat**—the country's most important crop—is grown by farmers to feed their families

- **Cotton-cloth manufacturing**—the country's second most important crop

- **Food processing**—for example, milling grains, refining sugar, and producing vegetable oil

- **Fertilizer production**

- **Cigarettes**

- **Carpets**

- **Steel**

_____

_____

_____

_____

_____

2. Describe the growth of agriculture in the ancient Indus Valley civilization.

_____

_____

_____

_____

CONTENT

Fill in the circle before the correct answer.

1. In ancient China oracle bones were used by the Shang people to _____.
   - (a) record history
   - (b) cure illnesses
   - (c) win wars
   - (d) predict the future

2. During which time period did rulers first apply Confucian ideas about fairness and learning?
   - (a) Qin dynasty
   - (b) Shang dynasty
   - (c) Han dynasty
   - (d) Huang civilization

3. What was the main form of agriculture on the steppes north of the Huang Valley?
   - (a) herding sheep and cattle
   - (b) growing rice and other grains
   - (c) raising horses
   - (d) cultivating fruits

4. Loess created problems for Huang Valley farmers because it _____.
   - (a) poisoned the water
   - (b) clogged irrigation ditches
   - (c) left fine silt on the fields
   - (d) soaked up all the rainwater

5. The ancient huts uncovered by archaeologists at Anyang were once used for _____.
   - (a) workshops
   - (b) prisons
   - (c) storehouses
   - (d) temples

Read each sentence and write the name from the box of the person it describes.

Fu Hao	Shihuangdi	Han Gaozu	Confucius	Wudi

6. This emperor of the Han dynasty created schools to prepare people for government jobs. _____

7. This teacher said that rulers must be wise and good, just as their subjects must be respectful. _____

8. Archaeologists found the tomb of this woman, who was a leader of troops, a ruler of her town, and a king's wife. _____

9. Although he was successful in creating a strong government, China's first emperor is remembered for his harsh rule. _____

10. This general was originally a farmer, before he led rebel armies to overthrow the Qin dynasty. _____

SKILLS

Read the passage below. Then answer the questions about writing a summary.

China is so large that many different forms of Chinese are spoken within its borders. People in one part of the country might not be able to understand people in another part. To help his people understand one another, an emperor named Shihuangdi set up a single system of writing that everyone in his empire could read. This form of writing, which is still used today, contains about 50,000 characters. It does not have an alphabet. In an alphabet each character stands for a sound. In Chinese each character stands for a thing or an idea, such as *house* or *down*. Using these characters, people in China could communicate with one another, even if they could not understand one another's spoken words. This standard form of writing helped Shihuangdi unite the people in such a vast region. It is one of the reasons the ancient nation of China has endured for so many centuries.

1. Which is the topic sentence of this passage?

    _____

    _____

    _____

2. What supporting details tell you that the emperor's system of writing was important to China?

    _____

    _____

3. Which sentence or sentences do not directly relate to the topic?

    _____

    _____

4. What is the purpose of the first sentence of this paragraph?

    _____

    _____

5. Write one or two sentences to summarize this passage.

    _____

    _____

    _____

WRITING

Write a short paragraph to answer each question. If you need more room, continue writing on the back of this page.

1. Explain how government was organized during the Han dynasty.

_____

_____

_____

_____

_____

_____

2. The three maps below make it clear that the growth of China was tied to control of the Huang and Chang rivers. Why was control of the rivers so important?

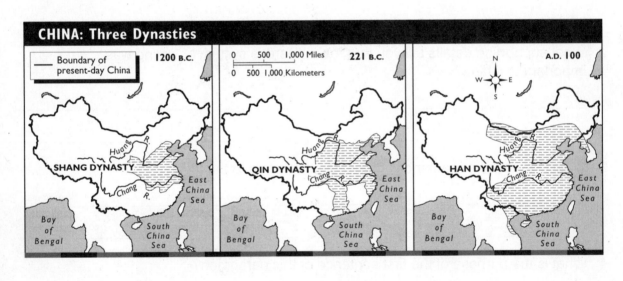

_____

_____

_____

_____

_____

_____

CONTENT

Fill in the circle before the correct answer.

1. Many physical features in the Americas were shaped by _____.
   - (a) glaciers
   - (b) rivers
   - (c) farming
   - (d) forests

2. Most of the Olmec were _____.
   - (a) rulers
   - (b) stone carvers
   - (c) traders
   - (d) farmers

3. Near the plaza at La Venta, archaeologists have discovered a mosaic in the image of _____.
   - (a) an Olmec ruler
   - (c) a jaguar
   - (b) an Olmec god
   - (d) an Olmec pyramid

4. When Jefferson and later archaeologists dug into the earthworks they discovered that _____.
   - (a) they were created by Europeans and Asians
   - (b) they were formed by nature
   - (c) many earthworks were burial mounds
   - (d) the Big Dipper appears directly above one of the mounds

5. Why are the different groups of the Hopewell classified together?
   - (a) they all spoke the same language
   - (b) they seemed to share the same religion and customs
   - (c) they all lived in the same place
   - (d) they were ruled by a single government

Write the word or term from the box that best completes each sentence.

isthmus	earthwork	totem	tropical	rain forest

6. The area of Earth near the equator is the _____ zone.

7. The Hopewell's _____ was a bear.

8. The part of Middle America that gets more rain than any other

   is the _____.

9. One _____ in Iowa is a group of 13 mounds arranged in a curve.

10. An _____ is a narrow strip of land that connects two larger land masses.

SKILLS

Use the climographs to answer the questions. Write your answers on the lines.

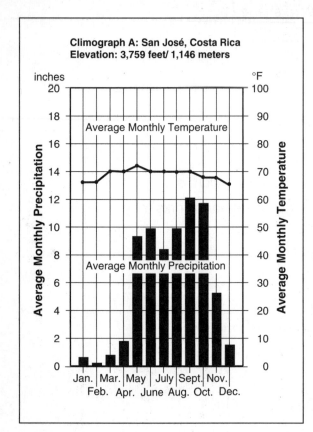

Source: *Great International Atlas*

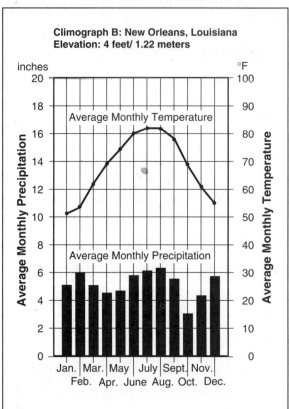

Source: *World Almanac and Book of Facts*, 1995

1. In which city does the amount of precipitation vary the most throughout the year?

                    _____

2. Which city has temperatures below 60°F during some months?

                    _____

3. In which month does New Orleans have the least precipitation?

                    _____

4. Which city has temperatures above 80°F in July and August?

                    _____

5. In which month does San José have the least precipitation?

                    _____

Name: _____   Date: _____

WRITING

Write a short paragraph to answer each question. If you need more room, continue writing on the back of this page.

1. Describe some of the artifacts discovered in La Venta and explain what they tell us about the Olmec.

_____
_____
_____
_____
_____

2. The picture below show a famous earthwork. It was discovered in Ohio, home of the Adena and Hopewell. Compare and contrast these two cultures.

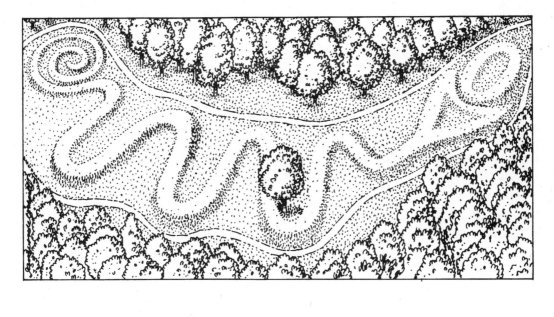

_____
_____
_____
_____
_____

CONTENT AND SKILLS

Fill in the circle before the correct answer.

1. A summary briefly states _____.
- (a) important dates
- (b) supporting details
- (c) opinions
- (d) main ideas

2. Why did crops grow quickly in the Indus Valley?
- (a) It had a hot climate.
- (b) There were frequent floods.
- (c) There were droughts.
- (d) Farmers used animals to pull plows.

3. Siddhartha Guatama founded _____.
- (a) Reincarnation
- (b) Hinduism
- (c) Buddhism
- (d) Aryanism

4. A climograph measures _____.
- (a) one day's precipitation
- (b) precipitation over time
- (c) temperature and precipitation over time
- (d) temperature over time

5. Confucius said good people would make _____.
- (a) a good civilization
- (b) a powerful dynasty
- (c) a large empire
- (d) good teachers

6. The city of Mohenjo-Daro _____.
- (a) was founded by Aryans
- (b) was very small
- (c) was carefully planned
- (d) had a weak government

7. The Olmec used a farming method known as _____.
- (a) levee
- (b) irrigation
- (c) slash and burn
- (d) desert highland

8. What two kinds of maps would you use to determine why a civilization settled in one particular region?
- (a) physical and agricultural
- (b) two maps of different scales
- (c) agricultural and political
- (d) political and physical

9. Who was China's first emperor?
- (a) Fu Hao
- (b) Shihuangdi
- (c) Han Gaozu
- (d) Wudi

10. The Vedas were the first building blocks of _____.
- (a) the Harappans
- (b) the Aryans
- (c) Confucianism
- (d) Hinduism

CONTENT AND SKILLS

Write the term from the box that best completes each sentence.

dharma	totem	steppes	mosaic	citadel
dynasty	isthmus	provinces	karma	levees

11. The Hindus' _____ was their laws and duties.

12. The bear was the _____ of the Hopewell.

13. The Shang _____ ruled for six hundred years.

14. The Qin empire was divided into thirty-six _____.

15. Archeologists discovered a large _____, or pattern of stones, at La Venta.

16. The dry, treeless plains that lie to the north of the Huang Valley are

    known as _____.

17. At the end of the Ice Age, rising waters covered land leaving

    only an _____ between North and South America.

18. About 3,000 years ago, farmers began building _____ to keep the Huang within its banks.

19. _____ is described by Hindus and Buddhists as a force caused by a person's good and bad acts.

20. Mohenjo-Daro had a _____, or large fort, at the west end of the city.

WRITING

Write a short paragraph to answer each question. If you need more room, continue writing on the back of this page.

1. Describe the origins and spread of Buddhism.

_____

_____

_____

_____

_____

_____

2. Use the chart below to help describe life in Mohenjo-Daro and the ancient Indus Valley civilization. What conclusions can you make from the information in the chart?

An Ancient City: Mohenjo-Daro

* carefully planned and built

* massive fort, or citadel

* remains of beautiful carvings, containers, paintings, and statues

* grain warehouses

_____

_____

_____

_____

_____

CONTENT

Fill in the circle before the correct answer.

1. Which of the following best describes the geography of ancient Canaan?
   - (a) rugged with varied climate
   - (b) lush and green
   - (c) flat and dry
   - (d) large fertile areas

2. What set the Hebrews apart from the other people in the Fertile Crescent?
   - (a) their farming techniques
   - (b) their belief in one God
   - (c) their belief in many gods
   - (d) their interest in Canaan

3. The sacred writings that form the basis of life and faith for the people of Israel are called _____.
   - (a) the decrees
   - (b) the covenant
   - (c) synagogues
   - (d) the Torah

4. Under King David, the Israelites _____.
   - (a) left Canaan
   - (b) became united
   - (c) wrote down the Torah
   - (d) divided into two nations

5. After the people of Judah and Israel split, they _____.
   - (a) were both conquered
   - (b) both prospered
   - (c) invaded other lands
   - (d) quickly reunited

Read each sentence and write the name from the box of the person it best describes.

| Abraham | Moses | David | Deborah | Solomon |

6. This judge or leader joined her followers with other Hebrew tribes in order to fight non-Jewish peoples. _____

7. This king of Israel may be most famous for his writing of poetry and proverbs. _____

8. This prophet led the Israelites out of slavery in Egypt. _____

9. This king of Israel conquered the Philistines. _____

10. This person traveled to ancient Canaan from the land of Mesopotamia. _____

SKILLS

Read the passage below about an archaeologist named Dr Garstang. Then answer the questions about identifying point of view.

"What patience an archaeologist must have!" exclaimed the tourist. "Aren't you bored sometimes?"

"Yes, it's tedious. It's like working out a gigantic jigsaw puzzle. But now and then it's very exciting!" [said Dr Garstang]

"And what do you think made the walls of Jericho fall down, Doctor?" asked the tourist.

[Dr Garstang replied] "I'm convinced it was a big earthquake. A similar earthquake occurred in this region not many years ago. Then the earthquake must have been followed by a great fire. The whole city seems to have been burnt. We have found ashes and burnt beams everywhere. And it all must have happened so quickly that the people in the city had to flee without being able to carry off their food. Nor have we found any signs of the city having been looted."

"This is very exciting," said the tourist.

From "The Drama of Ancient Israel" by John W. Flight, The Beacon Press, 1960

---

1. What subject is the archaeologist addressing?

   _____

2. What is Dr Garstang's opinion on archaeology?

   _____

3. What is Dr Garstang's point of view on the destruction of Jericho?

   _____

   _____

4. What words does the archaeologist use to describe and support his point of view?

   _____

   _____

5. What is the tourist's opinion on what Dr Garstang is saying?

   _____

   _____

WRITING

Write a short paragraph to answer each question. If you need more room, continue writing on the back of this page.

1. Compare and contrast the reigns of David and Solomon over the nation of Israel.

_____

_____

_____

_____

_____

2. Look at the map below. Explain how the geography of ancient Canaan affected the way people settled and lived there.

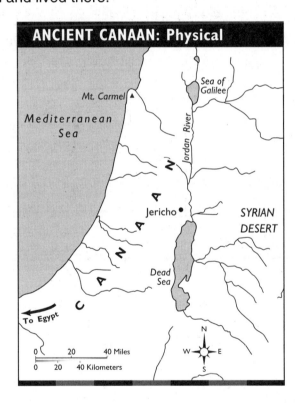

_____

_____

_____

_____

_____

CONTENT

Fill in the circle before the correct answer.

1. Like Greece, Phoenicia had a limited amount of _____.
   - (a) trade routes
   - (b) good farmland
   - (c) murex shells
   - (d) trees

2. Ancient Greeks got enough grain to eat by _____.
   - (a) planting it in early fall
   - (b) trading sheep and goats for it
   - (c) exchanging olive oil for it
   - (d) clearing forests for farmland

3. In 585 B.C. the Babylonians cut off the supply roads to _____.
   - (a) Tyre
   - (b) Phoenicia
   - (c) Assyria
   - (d) Canaan

4. The meeting place and market of a Greek city-state was known as the _____.
   - (a) agora
   - (b) polis
   - (c) acropolis
   - (d) colony

5. Sparta's people dedicated much of their lives to _____.
   - (a) farming
   - (b) trading
   - (c) reading and writing
   - (d) making their polis strong

Read each description and write the place in the box that it best describes.

| Sparta | Mount Olympus | Carthage | Strait of Gibraltar | Athens |

6. The largest city-state in ancient Greece. _____

7. According to legend, Dido founded this Phoenician city. _____

8. By 600 B.C. this Greek city-state was governed by an oligarchy. _____

9. This 8-mile-wide stretch of water separated Africa from Europe. _____

10. Home of the most powerful of the Greek gods. _____

Name: _____   Date: _____

SKILLS

Use the map below to help you answer the questions on historical maps.

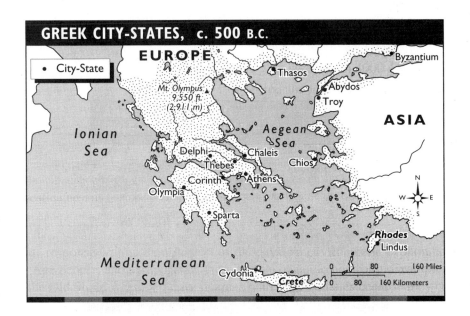

GREEK CITY-STATES, c. 500 B.C.

1. What makes the map above an historical map?

    _____

    _____

2. What information is contained in the map key?

    _____

3. What city-state developed on the island of Rhodes?

    _____

4. What is the approximate distance between Olympia and Corinth in miles?

    _____

5. What sea lies to the west of the Greek mainland?

    _____

WRITING

Write a short paragraph to answer each question. If you need more room,
continue writing on the back of this page.

1. Describe the different kinds of government that ancient Athens had.

_____

_____

_____

_____

_____

2. Use the map below to help explain the circumstances of Phoenicia's expansion to the
west. Describe the results of that expansion.

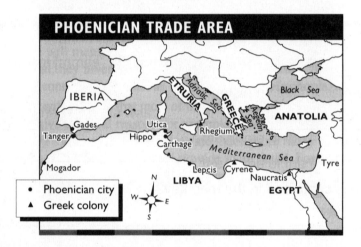

_____

_____

_____

_____

_____

CONTENT

Fill in the circle before the correct answer.

1. During Athens' Golden Age, new teachers taught different lessons, including _____.

- (a) debating and public speaking
- (b) running and wrestling
- (c) reading and writing
- (d) arithmetic

2. The Parthenon was built to honor _____.

- (a) Athenian citizens
- (b) Pericles
- (c) Socrates
- (d) Athena

3. Why did Athens surrender during the Peloponnesian War?

- (a) They were losing sea battles
- (b) They were losing land battles
- (c) Sparta cut off the Athenian grain supply
- (d) Sparta invaded the city

4. By 336 B.C. the army of _____ had taken over most of Greece.

- (a) Sparta
- (b) Macedonia
- (c) Athens
- (d) Persia

5. Why did the Greek alphabet make it easier for people to learn to read and write?

- (a) It was based on Egyptian hieroglyphics.
- (b) It was based on Mesopotamian cuneiform.
- (c) It had hundreds of symbols.
- (d) It had less than 30 letters.

Write the letter of the person that best fits each description.

6. _____ A Greek historian

7. _____ A ruler of Egypt

8. _____ A Macedonian king

9. _____ An Athenian leader

10. _____ A Greek philosopher

a. Socrates

b. Alexander

c. Thucydides

d. Pericles

e. Cleopatra

SKILLS

Read the passage below. It is about the "Elgin Marbles", a group of statues that were taken from the Parthenon in the early 1800s and shipped to England. Then answer the questions about identifying bias.

> The Parthenon marbles are our pride, our noblest symbol of excellence . . . . Greece has never ceased to ask for their return. [Some say] that more people could see the marbles if they were kept by the British Museum. By such logic, why not place them in permanent exhibit at Disneyland? Is it right that 95 percent of the Greek people might never see the finest of Greek creation?
>
> Melina Mercouri, former Greek minister of culture.

1. What is bias?

   _____

2. What clues, if any, can you find in the passage that indicate bias?

   _____

   _____

3. In your opinion, does the passage show a bias? Explain your answer.

   _____

   _____

   _____

4. Why do you think the writer of this passage may or may not be biased?

   _____

   _____

5. Why is it important to identify bias?

   _____

   _____

WRITING

Write a short paragraph to answer each question. If you need more room, continue writing on the back of this page.

1. Who was Pericles and what policies did he support?

_____

_____

_____

_____

_____

2. Use the map below to help you write a paragraph summarizing the details and effects of the Peloponnesian War.

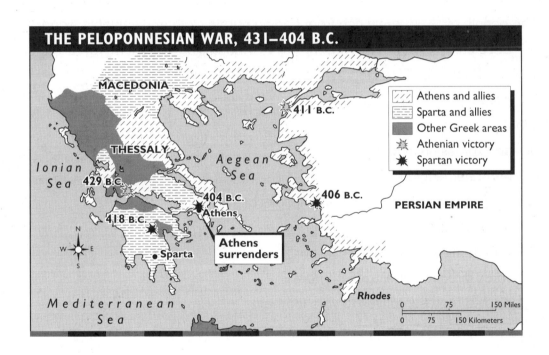

THE PELOPONNESIAN WAR, 431–404 B.C.

MACEDONIA
411 B.C.
THESSALY
Ionian Sea
429 B.C.
Aegean Sea
404 B.C.
Athens
406 B.C.
PERSIAN EMPIRE
418 B.C.
Athens surrenders
Sparta
Rhodes
Mediterranean Sea

Athens and allies
Sparta and allies
Other Greek areas
Athenian victory
Spartan victory

0   75   150 Miles
0   75   150 Kilometers

_____

_____

_____

_____

_____

CONTENT AND SKILLS

Fill in the circle before the correct answer.

1. The Peloponnesian War was fought between _____.

   (a) Athens and Sparta (c) Babylonia and Assyria

   (b) Phoenicia and Greece (d) Tyre and Carthage

2. What event occurred after King Solomon's death?

   (a) Israel and Judah united. (c) David became king.

   (b) Israel and Judah split. (d) The Hebrews settled Canaan.

3. Sparta set out to increase its military power after _____.

   (a) a slave revolt (c) an outbreak of disease

   (b) an Athenian invasion (d) Athens became a democracy

4. Which of the following might be found on an historical map of Phoenicia?

   (a) trade routes   (b) elevation   (c) railways   (d) rainfall

5. The people of _____ grew rich from trading purple cloth and valuable wood.

   (a) Babylonia   (b) Assyria   (c) Phoenicia   (d) Egypt

6. Which leader united the Hebrew people into one nation?

   (a) Abraham   (b) David   (c) Solomon   (d) Deborah

7. What is a person's point of view?

   (a) an expression of fact

   (b) his or her religion

   (c) the position from which a person looks at something

   (d) a biased account

8. During Athenian democracy, citizens _____.

   (a) voted directly in their government

   (b) elected representatives to vote for them

   (c) could not vote

   (d) could only vote if they were rich

9. Who became Egypt's ruler directly after Alexander's death?

   (a) Cleopatra   (b) Ptolemy   (c) Pericles   (d) Thucydides

10. Which of the statements below shows bias?

   (a) Athenians spent a great deal of time training.

   (b) The Peloponnesian War resulted in many losses.

   (c) Plato was a famous student of Socrates.

   (d) Alexander was the greatest leader of the ancient world.

CONTENT AND SKILLS

Write the term from the box that best fits each description. Write the term on the line.

jury	oasis	monotheism	oligarchy	polis
covenant	helot	prophet	tragedy	proverb

11. belief in only one god   _____

12. rule by a small group of rich citizens   _____

13. a brief, wise saying about human nature   _____

14. a Greek city-state   _____

15. a group of citizens chosen to hear evidence
    and make decisions in a court of law   _____

16. a serious play often showing Greek gods
    and their dealings with people   _____

17. a special agreement   _____

18. a person who speaks for God   _____

19. a slave in ancient Greece   _____

20. an area in the desert where a spring bubbles
    up from deep in the earth   _____

WRITING

Write a short paragraph to answer each question. If you need more room, continue writing on the back of this page.

1. Describe the importance of the arts and philosophy during the Golden Age of Athens.

_____

_____

_____

_____

_____

_____

2. The excerpt below describes Moses receiving the Ten Commandments on Mount Sinai.

> When the Lord descended upon Mount Sinai, to the top of the mountain, the Lord summoned Moses to the top of the mountain and Moses went up . . . . Then God spoke all these words: "I am the Lord your God, who brought you out of the land of Egypt, out of the house of slavery, you shall have no other gods before me . . . . For I the Lord your God [show] steadfast love to the thousandth generation of those who love me and keep my commandments."

Exodus, 19:20, 20:1-3, 5-6

What are some of the basic elements of Hebrew law and how are they important to the Hebrew people?

_____

_____

_____

_____

_____

_____

CONTENT

Fill in the circle before the correct answer.

1. Sicily was a popular destination for ancient Greek colonists because it _____.
   - (a) had a good climate
   - (b) was near Rome
   - (c) had many trade routes
   - (d) had rich farmland

2. What makes it difficult to travel across the Italian peninsula?
   - (a) the Alps
   - (b) the Tiber
   - (c) the Apennines
   - (d) the Latium plain

3. According to legend, Romulus and Remus founded a new city _____.
   - (a) on the hill where they were rescued
   - (b) in the place they had been born
   - (c) where the former king was born
   - (d) where their father died

4. Rome's plebeians were _____.
   - (a) a group of nobles
   - (b) slaves
   - (c) farmers, traders and craftworkers
   - (d) government leaders

5. Why did Hannibal decide to attack Rome by land?
   - (a) He had no navy.
   - (b) Rome's navy controlled the waters around Italy.
   - (c) His father, a general, advised him.
   - (d) It was quicker to travel by land.

Write the word or term from the box that best completes each sentence.

| tribunes | Senate | consuls | patricians | republic |

6. In Rome, the _____ came from the city's noble families.

7. Under the Roman system of government, the _____ worked to gain rights for the plebeians.

8. In a _____, citizens choose their leaders.

9. Rome's _____ determined how Rome would act towards other governments.

10. _____ served as Rome's army commanders and the city's most powerful judges.

SKILLS

Use the elevation map of Italy to answer the questions.

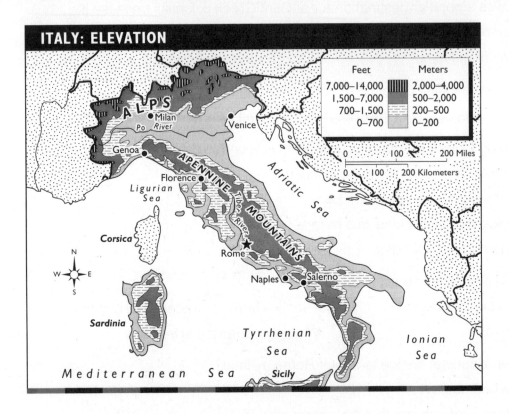

ITALY: ELEVATION

Feet		Meters
7,000–14,000	‖‖‖	2,000–4,000
1,500–7,000		500–2,000
700–1,500		200–500
0–700		0–200

1. In what part of Italy are the highest elevations? _____

2. What is the elevation of Venice? _____

3. What is the elevation of the Apennines? _____

4. How is this elevation map similar to a profile map?

_____

5. What could a profile map of Italy show better than this elevation map?

_____

WRITING

Write a short paragraph to answer each question. If you need more room, continue writing on the back of this page.

1. Describe the geography of Italy.

_____

_____

_____

_____

_____

2. Read the passage below. It was written by Cicero, one of Rome's greatest statesmen.

. . . those whom Nature has endowed with [given] the capacity for administering public affairs should put aside all hesitation, enter the race for public office, and take a hand in directing the government; for in no other way can a government be administered or greatness of spirit be made manifest [obvious].

Explain how the citizens of ancient Rome took "a hand in directing the government."

_____

_____

_____

_____

_____

CONTENT

Fill in the circle before the correct answer.

1. Julius Caesar created the basis for the _____ that we still use today.

(a) calendar   (b) census   (c) Senate   (d) government

2. Augustus worked to create a strong _____.

(a) army   (c) central government

(b) republic   (d) trading system

3. Why did Mary and Joseph go to Bethlehem?

(a) God had called them there.

(b) They were fleeing a war.

(c) Augustus had ordered a census.

(d) They went to celebrate Passover.

4. The Roman empire was reunited under the rule of _____.

(a) Julius Caesar (b) Augustus   (c) Diocletian   (d) Constantine

5. Roman letters were first written only in _____.

(a) basilicas   (c) coliseums

(b) courts   (d) capital-letter form

Write **true** or **false** next to each statement.

6. _____   Trade was restricted during the Pax Romana.

7. _____   Diocletian divided the Roman empire into four parts.

8. _____   Rome left behind powerful legacies in the fields of government and architecture.

9. _____   Cement is a building material invented by the Romans and still used today.

10. _____   The emperor Constantine became a supporter of Christianity.

SKILLS

Read the passage below. It was written by Tacitus, a Roman historian, and discusses the fire of A.D. 64, which some people had suggested was started by the emperor Nero.

> Whether [the fire was] the result of accident or of the emperor's guile [cunning] is uncertain as authors have given both versions . . . . It started first in the part of the Circus which adjoins the Palatine . . . where, amid the shops containing inflammable wares, the conflagration [fire] broke out, instantly gathered strength, and, driven by the wind, swept down the length of the Circus.

1. What can evaluating the reliability of this source help you do?

   _____

2. Does the author have first-hand experience of the subject? Explain.

   _____

3. Do you think this source is reliable? Why or why not?

   _____

   _____

4. Does Tacitus support the emperor? Or oppose him? Or neither? Explain your answer.

   _____

   _____

5. Tacitus gives details about the fire. Does this make his source seem more or less reliable? Why?

   _____

   _____

WRITING

Write a short paragraph to answer each question. If you need more room, continue writing on the back of this page.

1. What was the Pax Romana? Describe some of the changes that took place during this period. Use the time line below to help you answer the question.

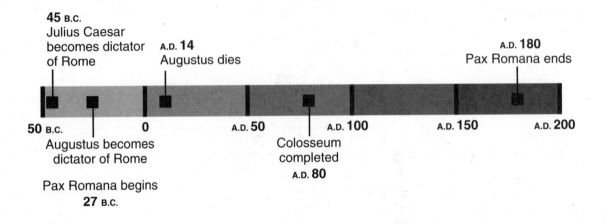

45 B.C.
Julius Caesar
becomes dictator   A.D. 14
of Rome   Augustus dies   A.D. 180
                                                                       Pax Romana ends

50 B.C.   0   A.D. 50   A.D. 100   A.D. 150   A.D. 200

Augustus becomes   Colosseum
dictator of Rome   completed
                                   A.D. 80
Pax Romana begins
27 B.C.

_____

_____

_____

_____

_____

2. Compare how the Romans treated Christians before and after the reign of Constantine.

_____

_____

_____

_____

_____

CONTENT AND SKILLS

Fill in the circle before the correct answer.

1. The city of Rome developed over seven _____.
   - (a) rivers
   - (b) lakes
   - (c) hills
   - (d) roads

2. One of the most important crops in ancient Rome was _____.
   - (a) wine grapes
   - (b) wheat
   - (c) figs
   - (d) lettuce

3. Elevation and profile maps show the _____.
   - (a) varying heights of a region
   - (b) distances between rivers
   - (c) length of time it takes to travel from one place to another
   - (d) height below sea level

4. The oldest and most powerful branch of the Roman republic was _____.
   - (a) the tribunes
   - (b) the Senate
   - (c) the citizen assembly
   - (d) the consuls

5. Evaluating a source's reliability helps you _____.
   - (a) decide if it's a primary source
   - (b) figure out if you can trust its accuracy
   - (c) write a biased account
   - (d) research a topic

6. The Pantheon was a temple that honored _____.
   - (a) Isis
   - (b) Augustus
   - (c) Julius Caesar
   - (d) all the gods of the Roman world

7. Jesus often used _____, or stories containing simple truths, to teach his followers.
   - (a) parables
   - (b) the Ten Commandments
   - (c) apostles
   - (d) the New Testament

8. Constantinople was surrounded on three sides by _____.
   - (a) walls
   - (b) mountains
   - (c) water
   - (d) plains

9. In Roman numbers, "X" stands for _____.
   - (a) 5
   - (b) 10
   - (c) 50
   - (d) 100

10. According to legend, one of the founders of Rome was _____.
    - (a) Constantine
    - (b) Julius Caesar
    - (c) Remus
    - (d) Diocletian

CONTENT AND SKILLS

Write the name from the box that best fits each description.

Paul	Carthage	Gaul	Augustus	Hannibal
Colosseum	Latium	Diocletian	Nazareth	Forum

---

11. Octavian took this name, meaning "honored one."   _____

12. A clearing that was the center of life in Rome.   _____

13. The Roman emperor who divided the empire into two parts.   _____

14. Julius Caesar was military governor of this country, which is now France.   _____

15. This empire fought with Rome during the Punic Wars.   _____

16. Some people believe that this person became the first bishop of Rome.   _____

17. This is the name of one of Italy's fertile plains.   _____

18. He invaded Rome with elephants.   _____

19. Jesus lived here with his family.   _____

20. This was the largest stadium in Rome.   _____

WRITING

Write a short paragraph to answer each question. If you need more room, continue writing on the back of this page.

1. Read this version of a speech that Julius Caesar made to the Roman Senate in 63 B.C.

   Our ancestors were good at planning and full of courage in action. They also imitated whatever was worthwhile in the culture of other nations. For example, they copied the armor and weapons of the Samnites. Their official robes and symbols came from the Etruscans. In fact, they eagerly imitated any promising idea, whether it came from a friend or an enemy.

   Think of two "promising ideas" developed by the Romans that are imitated or used by people today. Describe each idea and explain why it is still useful and important to modern people.

   _____

   _____

   _____

   _____

   _____

   _____

   _____

   _____

   _____

2. In your opinion were most Romans better off during the years of the republic or during the Pax Romana? Give reasons to support your answer.

   _____

   _____

   _____

   _____

   _____

   _____

   _____

   _____

Part 4

Performance Assessments

Contents

Performance Assessment

Chapter 1: Writing a Paragraph of Description

Goal

The student will write a paragraph describing the region in which he or she lives.

Suggestions:

1. Have students review Lesson 1 and brainstorm a list of features in the region.

2. Model the process by describing another region where you have lived or that you have visited.

Portfolio Opportunities

Have students exchange descriptions with their partners and evaluate the descriptions by writing a sentence telling what is best about the description. Then have students display their descriptions or place them in their portfolios with the partner's comments.

SCORING RUBRIC

4 An **excellent** description clearly describes at least five important characteristics of the region, including major landforms, climate, and aspects of culture. The paragraph has a main idea or topic sentence and at least three supporting detail sentences, it uses strong visual language, and it presents information in a logical order. The description is written with correct use of conventions (grammar, punctuation, capitalization, and spelling).

3 A **good** description clearly describes four important characteristics of the region, including major landforms, climate, and aspects of culture. The paragraph has a main idea or topic sentence and at least two supporting detail sentences, it uses strong visual language, and it presents information in a logical order. The description is written with generally correct use of conventions.

2 A **fair** description clearly describes three important characteristics of the region, including major landforms, climate, and aspects of culture. The paragraph has a main idea or topic sentence, but it may not be written clearly. Details may not be presented in a logical order, or the paragraph may include some inaccurate information. The description may include some errors in the use of conventions.

1 A **poor** description describes only one or two characteristics of the region, or it presents inaccurate information.

0 An **unscorable** description is unreadable or is not related to the region.

Performance Assessment

Chapter 1: Writing a Letter

Goal

The student will describe the culture and values of his or her community in a letter to Azeez Narain in India.

Suggestions:

1. Review Lesson 2 and have students discuss the culture and values of the community.
2. Model the process by writing a letter about your community to a friend or colleague in a distant place.

Portfolio Opportunities

Have students exchange letters and evaluate the letters by completing peer assessment forms. Then have students place their letters and peer assessments in their portfolios.

SCORING RUBRIC

4 An **excellent** letter clearly describes at least four aspects of the culture and values in the student's community and tells at least two ways in which the student's life is similar to or different from Azeez Narain's life. The letter is addressed to Azeez Narain and includes five parts of a letter (date, salutation, body, closing, and signature). It presents information in a logical order and clearly indicates comparisons and contrasts between life in the two communities. The letter is written with correct use of conventions (grammar, punctuation, capitalization, and spelling).

3 A **good** letter clearly describes three aspects of the culture and values in the student's community and tells at least two ways in which the student's life is similar to or different from Azeez Narain's life. The letter is addressed to Azeez Narain and includes four or five parts of a letter (date, salutation, body, closing, and signature). It presents information in a logical order and clearly indicates comparisons and contrasts between life in the two communities. The letter is written with generally correct use of conventions.

2 A **fair** letter describes two aspects of the culture and values in the student's community and tells at least one way in which the student's life is similar to or different from Azeez Narain's life. The letter is addressed to Azeez Narain and includes three or four parts of a letter (date, salutation, body, closing, and signature). It may not present information in a logical order or clearly indicate comparisons and contrasts. The letter may include some errors in the use of conventions.

1 A **poor** letter is not written to Azeez Narain, does not describe aspects of the culture and values in the student's community, or it presents generally inaccurate information.

0 An **unscorable** letter is incomplete or is not related to the subject.

Performance Assessment

Chapter 1: Writing a Travel Pamphlet

Goal
The student will write a travel pamphlet about an interesting place she or he has visited.

Suggestions:
1. Bring in and share pictures of an interesting place and have students discuss how they might present this attraction in a travel pamphlet.

2. Model the process by bringing in and sharing a travel pamphlet about an interesting place.

Portfolio Opportunities
Have students work in small groups to present their travel pamphlets and complete peer assessment forms to evaluate one another's work. Then have students display their pamphlets and place the peer assessment forms in their portfolios.

SCORING RUBRIC

4 An **excellent** pamphlet uses strong illustrations or other visuals and concise text to describe an interesting place the student has visited. It describes at least four features of the place and presents information in a logical order. It is written for a person from another country who will visit the place. The pamphlet is written with correct use of conventions (grammar, punctuation, capitalization, and spelling).

3 A **good** pamphlet uses a strong illustration or other visual and concise text to describe an interesting place the student has visited. It describes three features of the place and presents information in a logical order. It is written for a person from another country who will visit the place. The pamphlet is written with generally correct use of conventions.

2 A **fair** pamphlet uses an illustration or other visual and includes text to describe an interesting place the student has visited. It describes two features of the place, but information may not be presented in a logical order. It may not be clearly addressed to a person from another country who will visit the place. The pamphlet may include some errors in the use of conventions.

1 A **poor** pamphlet does not have a visual, does not include text describing a place, or does not present accurate information about a location.

0 An **unscorable** pamphlet is incomplete, it is not presented as a pamphlet, or it does not relate to an interesting place.

Performance Assessment

Chapter 2: Writing a Summary

Goal

The student will write a paragraph summarizing the history of the community.

Suggestions:

1. Have students review Lesson 1 and discuss what they know about the history of the community.

2. Model the process by reading a summary of an event that took place in the community.

Portfolio Opportunities

Have students exchange summaries with their partners and evaluate the summaries by writing one or two sentences telling what is good about the summary and what might be improved. Then have students display their summaries or place them in their portfolios with the partner's comments.

SCORING RUBRIC

4 An **excellent** summary clearly describes at least five important aspects of the community's history. The summary has a main idea or topic sentence and at least three supporting detail sentences, and it presents information in a logical order. The summary is written with correct use of conventions (grammar, punctuation, capitalization, and spelling).

3 A **good** summary clearly describes four important aspects of the community's history. The paragraph has a main idea or topic sentence and at least two supporting detail sentences, and it presents information in a logical order. The summary is written with generally correct use of conventions.

2 A **fair** summary clearly describes three important aspects of the community's history. The summary has a main idea or topic sentence, but it may not be written clearly. Details may not be presented in a logical order, or the summary may include some inaccurate information. The summary may include some errors in the use of conventions.

1 A **poor** summary describes only one or two aspects of the community's history, or it presents inaccurate information.

0 An **unscorable** summary is unreadable or is not related to the community's history.

Performance Assessment

Chapter 2: Writing an Article

Goal

The student will write an article for a school newspaper about "The Iceman of the Alps."

Suggestions:

1. Review Lesson 2 and have students discuss what an article about the Iceman might include.

2. Model the process by bringing in and sharing an article on another subject, preferably from a school newspaper.

Portfolio Opportunities

Have students work in small groups to present their articles and complete peer assessment forms to evaluate one another's work. Then have students place their articles in their portfolios with the peer assessment forms.

SCORING RUBRIC

4 An **excellent** article tells who, what, when, where, and why in a logical order with correct use of conventions (grammar, punctuation, capitalization, and spelling). It describes at least three details about the discovery of the Iceman and at least three details of what archaeologists learned from it. Example: The Iceman was discovered by Erika and Helmut Simon in the Alps in September 1991. The body and its clothing were intact and several items lay nearby, including a knife, bits of rope and leather, an ax, hunting arrows, and a net. German archaeologist Konrad Spindler came to investigate. Eventually, testing revealed that the Iceman lived about 5,300 years ago. From studying the remains of the Iceman, archaeologists concluded that the people of his time were experts at interacting with their environment, they were skilled metalworkers, they had a form of matches and some forms of medicine, and they had contact with farmers who raised grain.

3 A **good** article reflects four of the 5 Ws in a logical order with generally correct use of conventions. It describes two or three details about the discovery of the Iceman and two or three details about what archaeologists learned from it.

2 A **fair** article reflects two or three of the 5 Ws, although the information may not be presented in a logical order. It describes two details about the discovery of the Iceman and one or two details about what archaeologists learned from it. The article may include some errors in the use of conventions.

1 A **poor** article may describe the discovery of the Iceman in a general way, but it does not describe who, when, where, or why, or it presents inaccurate information.

0 An **unscorable** article is unreadable or has nothing to do with the Iceman.

Performance Assessment

Chapter 2: Writing an Interview

Goal
The student writes an interview with the Iceman.

Suggestions:
1. Review Lesson 2 and discuss the kinds of questions one might ask the Iceman.

2. Model the process by playing the role of a person who lived in prehistoric times and having students ask you questions.

Portfolio Opportunities
Have students evaluate their own interviews by using them to role-play with partners and discussing what is good about them and what might be improved. Then have students share their interviews with the class and place the interviews in their portfolios.

SCORING RUBRIC

4 An **excellent** interview has at least five well-written questions that are easy to understand, are specific to the Iceman, lead to informative responses, and are presented in a logical sequence. Questions might focus on the Iceman's clothing and equipment, how he made and used his tools, what he ate and did, where he had traveled and why, how he was injured, and what happened in the place where he was found. The interview also provides reasonable responses to the questions from the Iceman's point of view. The questions and answers in the interview are clearly labeled, and the interview is written with correct use of conventions (grammar, punctuation, capitalization, and spelling).

3 A **good** interview has four well-written questions that are easy to understand, are specific to the Iceman, lead to informative responses, and are presented in a logical sequence. The interview also provides reasonable responses to the questions from the Iceman's point of view. The questions and answers in the interview are clearly labeled, and the interview is written with generally correct use of conventions.

2 A **fair** interview has two or three well-written questions that are easy to understand, are specific to the Iceman, and lead to informative responses. The questions may not be presented in a logical sequence, or they may include questions that are not appropriate to the topic. The interview provides reasonable responses to the questions from the Iceman's point of view, although they may include some inaccurate information. The questions and answers in the interview may not be clearly labeled, and the interview may include some errors in the use of conventions.

1 A **poor** interview does not have clear, focused questions and does not lead to informative responses.

0 An **unscorable** interview is unreadable, is not written as an interview, or does not have anything to do with the Iceman.

Performance Assessment

Unit 1 Review Project: Design Your Own Region

Goal

The student will demonstrate an understanding of landforms by working with a group to design and create a region.

Suggestions:

1. Have students discuss the landforms mentioned in the unit and the characteristics of a geographical region.

2. Model the process by giving an example of landforms you would want in a region you design.

Portfolio Opportunities

Have students exchange models with other groups and evaluate the regions by using the questions on the peer assessment form. Then have students display their models and place the peer assessments in their portfolios. For individual assessment have each student complete a self-assessment form to evaluate his or her contribution to the project.

SCORING RUBRIC

4 An **excellent** project presents a clay model of a new region with at least five different landforms, an accurate label for each landform, and a name for the region. It also includes a clear and accurate description of the region on an index card. The model of the region is well constructed and decorated in a creative way, and it presents integrated concepts of how the landforms in a region fit together. The text of the description is written with correct use of conventions (grammar, punctuation, capitalization, and spelling).

3 A **good** project presents a clay model of a new region with four or five different landforms, an accurate label for each landform, and a name for the region. It also includes a clear and accurate description of the region on an index card. The model of the region is fairly well constructed and presents integrated concepts of how the landforms in a region fit together. The text of the description is written with generally correct use of conventions.

2 A **fair** project presents a clay model of a new region with three or four different landforms, an accurate label for each landform, and a name for the region. It also includes a description of the region on an index card, although the description may not be particularly accurate or complete. The model of the region is fairly well constructed, but it may not present integrated concepts of how the landforms in a region fit together. The text of the description may include some errors in the use of conventions.

1 A **poor** project has only one or two landforms, it does not have a clear description of the region, or it depicts inaccurate information.

0 An **unscorable** project is incomplete, is not presented as a clay model, or has nothing to do with landforms.

Performance Assessment

Chapter 3: Writing About a Family

Goal

The student will write a paragraph about how the Leakey family's discoveries contributed to a better understanding of our early ancestors.

Suggestions:

1. Review Lesson 1 and have students discuss the achievements of the Leakey family.

2. Model the process by writing or bringing in and sharing a paragraph describing the achievements of another person or family.

Portfolio Opportunities

Have students evaluate their own paragraphs by telling what they like best about them. Then have students collect their paragraphs in a notebook or place them in their portfolios.

SCORING RUBRIC

4 An **excellent** paragraph has a main idea or topic sentence and three or more sentences with supporting information. The main idea or topic sentence clearly states a perspective on the Leakey family and their contributions to a better understanding or our early ancestors. The rest of the paragraph gives supporting details. Examples: Louis and Mary Leakey began searching for evidence of early human life in the Olduvai Gorge in the 1930s. In 1959, Mary Leakey found parts of a skull of an early human ancestor dating back 1.75 million years. Louis and Mary named this ancestor *Australopithecus.* In 1960, the Leakeys' son, Jonathan, found a 2.2-million-year-old skull. His father named the new ancestor *Homo habilis*, or "handy man." *Homo habilis* was the first ancestor to belong to the same group as modern humans. The paragraph is written with correct use of conventions (grammar, punctuation, capitalization, and spelling).

3 A **good** paragraph has a main idea or topic sentence and two sentences with supporting information. The main idea or topic sentence clearly states a perspective on the Leakey family and their contributions to a better understanding of our early ancestors. The rest of the paragraph gives supporting details. The paragraph is written with generally correct use of conventions.

2 A **fair** paragraph has a main idea or topic sentence and at least one sentence with supporting information about the Leakey family and their contributions to a better understanding of our early ancestors. The main idea or topic sentence may not be stated clearly. The supporting sentences may include information that is not clearly related to the main idea. The paragraph may include some errors in the use of conventions.

1 A **poor** paragraph does not have a main idea or topic sentence, or it does not have supporting information. The paragraph does not describe the Leakey family's contributions to a better understanding of our early ancestors.

0 An **unscorable** paragraph is unreadable or does not relate to the task.

Performance Assessment

Chapter 3: Writing About a Place

Goal

The student writes one or two paragraphs about Border Cave, how the people who lived there survived, and what they ate.

Suggestions:

1. Review Lesson 2 and have students discuss how the people of Border Cave lived.

2. Model the process by writing or sharing a description of another group of people and their way of life, such as the Cro-Magnon.

Portfolio Opportunities

Have students exchange paragraphs with their partners and evaluate the paragraphs by writing a sentence telling what is best about the description. Then have students display their paragraphs or place them in their portfolios with partners' comments.

SCORING RUBRIC

4 An **excellent** paragraph has a main idea or topic sentence and supporting sentences describing at least five characteristics of Border Cave, its people, and their way of life. The main idea or topic sentence clearly states a perspective on the people of Border Cave. Supporting sentences include descriptive details. Examples: Border Cave is located in the side of a cliff in the northeastern part of South Africa. It overlooks a grassy river valley which served as a base for hunter-gatherers who hunted eland. The people may have used bows and arrows for hunting, slept on grass bedding, and made campfires for cooking and light. The people of Border Cave also gathered fruits and other kinds of plants for food. The discovery of a seashell bead suggests that they appreciated beauty and may have had religious beliefs. The paragraph is written with correct use of conventions (grammar, punctuation, capitalization, and spelling).

3 A **good** paragraph has a main idea or topic sentence and supporting sentences describing three or four characteristics of Border Cave, its people, and their way of life. The main idea or topic sentence clearly states a perspective on the people of Border Cave. Supporting sentences include descriptive details. The paragraph is written with generally correct use of conventions.

2 A **fair** paragraph has a main idea or topic sentence and supporting sentences describing at least two characteristics of Border Cave, its people, and their way of life. The main idea or topic sentence may not be clearly stated. The supporting sentences may include information that is not clearly related to the main idea. The paragraph may include some errors in the use of conventions.

1 A **poor** paragraph does not have a main idea or topic sentence, or it does not have supporting information. The paragraph does not describe the people of Border Cave and how they lived.

0 An **unscorable** paragraph is unreadable or does not relate to the task.

Performance Assessment

Chapter 3: Writing a Report

Goal

The student writes a report on the Ice Age and explains why scientists think that the migration of peoples to the Americas occurred during this period.

Suggestions:

1. Review Lesson 3 and have students discuss the evidence suggesting that peoples migrated to the Americas during the Ice Age.

2. Model the process by giving an example of one piece of evidence and explaining how it supports the scientists' theories.

Portfolio Opportunities

Have students evaluate their own reports by completing self-assessment forms. Then have students collect their reports in a notebook or place them in their portfolios with the self-assessments.

SCORING RUBRIC

4 An **excellent** report clearly explains why scientists believe that people migrated to the Americas during the Ice Age and gives at least three factors or reasons supporting this idea. The report clearly states the topic in a main idea or topic sentence and presents information in a logical order. Examples: Asia and the Americas are separated by vast oceans, and the peoples of ancient times had no large ships. However, during the Ice Age when so much of Earth's water was frozen, the sea level dropped. Many land masses were exposed, including a land bridge called Beringia that connected Asia with present-day Alaska. Scientists believe that peoples migrated from Asia to the Americas during the Ice Age when Beringia was exposed. Fossil evidence connects people of both continents. The report is written with correct use of conventions (grammar, punctuation, capitalization, and spelling).

3 A **good** report clearly explains why scientists believe that people migrated to the Americas during the Ice Age and gives two factors or reasons supporting this idea. The report clearly states the topic in a main idea or topic sentence and presents information in a logical order. The report is written with generally correct use of conventions.

2 A **fair** report explains why scientists believe that people migrated to the Americas during the Ice Age and gives one factor or reason supporting this idea. The report relates to the topic, but the topic may not be clearly stated. Information may not be presented in a logical order. The report may include some errors in the use of conventions.

1 A **poor** report docs not explain why scientists believe that people migrated to the Americas during the Ice Age.

0 An **unscorable** report is incomplete or unreadable or does not relate to the topic.

Performance Assessment

Chapter 4: Writing a Journal Entry

Goal

The student will describe living in Catal Huyuk during the New Stone Age by writing a journal entry.

Suggestions:

1. Review Lesson 1, including the diagram of Catal Huyuk on page 80, and have students brainstorm a list of descriptive details about how people lived and what they did.

2. Model the process by writing and sharing a journal entry about how you might have worked as a teacher in Catal Huyuk.

Portfolio Opportunities

Have students exchange journal entries with partners and write a sentence describing what they like best about the partner's journal entry. Then have students display their journal entries with pictures of Catal Huyuk or place them in their porfolios with partners' comments included.

SCORING RUBRIC

4 An **excellent** journal entry gives specific details about living in Catal Huyuk during the New Stone Age and includes at least five personal observations about how the person lived, the work he or she did, and the people he or she might have seen. Examples: The people lived in houses with brick and plaster walls covered by flat reed roofs. They entered the home through an opening in the roof, used a fireplace and oven for heating and cooking, and slept on raised platforms with reed mats. Some people worked as farmers, while others specialized in making things such as tools, bricks, cloth, and pots. Other items mentioned may include wool, copper, jewelry, and obsidian. A person living in Catal Huyuk might have seen craftworkers, farmers, travelers, and traders from other parts of the area and lands as far away as present-day Syria. The journal entry is written with correct use of conventions (grammar, punctuation, capitalization, and spelling).

3 A **good** journal entry gives specific details about living in Catal Huyuk during the New Stone Age and includes three or four personal observations about how the person lived, the work he or she did, and the people he or she might have seen. The journal entry is written with generally correct use of conventions.

2 A **fair** journal entry gives some specific details about living in Catal Huyuk during the New Stone Age and includes one or two personal observations about how the person lived, the work he or she did, and the people he or she might have seen. The journal entry may include some inaccurate information, and it may include some errors in the use of conventions.

1 A **poor** journal entry does not include specific details about living in Catal Huyuk during the New Stone Age, or all of the descriptive information is inaccurate.

0 An **unscorable** journal entry is unreadable or does not relate to the task.

Performance Assessment

Chapter 4: Writing a List

Goal

The student shows an understanding of New Stone Age agriculture by making a list of plants and animals that were domesticated by early farmers and what they were used for.

Suggestions:

1. Have students discuss the meaning of *domestication* and give examples of plants and animals that were domesticated during the New Stone Age.

2. Model the process by describing domesticated plants and animals that are familiar to us today.

Portfolio Opportunities

Have students exchange lists with partners and evaluate the lists by completing peer assessment forms. Then have students display their lists on a bulletin board or place them in their portfolios with completed peer assessments.

SCORING RUBRIC

4 An **excellent** list names two plants and two animals that were domesticated during the New Stone Age and includes one or two sentences explaining how the plants and animals were used. Examples: Wheat, barley, peas, and lentils were domesticated along with sheep, cattle, pigs, and goats. Sheep provided New Stone Age people with wool for cloth. Cattle provided a steady supply of milk and meat. Grains such as wheat were used to make bread. The text is written with correct use of conventions (grammar, punctuation, capitalization, and spelling).

3 A **good** list names two plants and two animals that were domesticated during the New Stone Age and includes a sentence that explains how these resources were used. The text is written with generally correct use of conventions.

2 A **fair** list names two plants and two animals that were domesticated during the New Stone Age. It may not include information that explains how these plants and animals were used, or the information may be inaccurate. The text may include some errors in the use of conventions.

1 A **poor** list does not name plants or animals that were domesticated during the New Stone Age.

0 An **unscorable** list does not relate to the topic or is unreadable.

Performance Assessment

Chapter 4: Writing a Summary

Goal

The student writes a paragraph summarizing the arguments of those who claim that the change from hunting and gathering to farming was an important step in the development of civilization.

Suggestions:

1. Review the chapter and have students identify arguments supporting the idea that the change from hunting and gathering to farming was an important step.

2. Model the process by giving an example of an important change in a specific culture brought about by an agricultural development.

Portfolio Opportunities

Have students exchange paragraphs with their partners and evaluate the summaries by writing one or two sentences telling what is good about the summary and what might be improved. Then have students display their summaries or place them in their portfolios with partners' comments.

SCORING RUBRIC

4 An **excellent** summary clearly describes at least four arguments supporting the idea that the change from hunting and gathering to farming was an important step in the development of civilization. The summary has a main idea or topic sentence and at least three supporting sentences, and it presents information in a logical order. Example: Agriculture provided a way for people to live in large groups without having to travel great distances to gather food. With farmers producing enough food for the people in a group, other members of the group could specialize and develop skills in other trades and crafts. This development, in turn, led to trade with other peoples and new ways of organizing communities. The growth of larger populations led to the need for a leader to make community decisions. The summary may include that the development in agriculture led to a new civilization. The summary is written with correct use of conventions (grammar, punctuation, capitalization, and spelling).

3 A **good** summary clearly describes three arguments supporting the idea that the change from hunting and gathering to farming was an important step in the development of civilization. The summary has a main idea or topic sentence and at least two supporting sentences, and it presents information in a logical order. The summary is written with generally correct use of conventions.

2 A **fair** summary describes one or two arguments supporting the idea that the change from hunting and gathering to farming was an important step in the development of civilization. The summary has a main idea or topic sentence, but it may not be written clearly. Supporting details may not be presented in a logical order, or the summary may include some inaccurate information. The summary may include some errors in the use of conventions.

1 A **poor** summary does not describe arguments supporting the idea that the change from hunting and gathering to farming was an important step, or it presents inaccurate information.

0 An **unscorable** summary is unreadable or does not have anything to do with agriculture's effect on the development of civilization.

Performance Assessment

Unit 2 Project: Farming Methods Old and New

Goal
The student will show an understanding of farming methods old and new by creating a poster.

Suggestions:
1. Have students review Chapter 4 and take notes on different farming methods.

2. Model the process by comparing an early farming method with a modern farming method.

Portfolio Opportunities
Have students evaluate their posters by completing self-assessment forms. Have students display their posters and place their self-assessments in their portfolios.

SCORING RUBRIC

4 An **excellent** poster includes a list of at least five early farming methods (such as planting seeds by hand, slash and burn, and terracing) and at least five modern farming methods (such as crop rotation, the use of chemical or organic fertilizers, and the use of machinery). The poster reflects the results of research, and it includes accurate pictures or drawings, descriptive labels, and descriptions of methods. The poster is presented in a colorful and creative way, and the text is written with correct use of conventions (grammar, punctuation, capitalization, and spelling).

3 A **good** poster includes a list of three or four early farming methods and three or four modern farming methods. The poster reflects the results of research, and it includes accurate pictures or drawings, descriptive labels, and descriptions of methods. The poster is presented in a somewhat creative way, and the text is written with generally correct use of conventions.

2 A **fair** poster includes a list of at least two early farming methods and at least two modern farming methods. The poster may not reflect the results of research, and it may include inaccurate information. The text may include some errors in the use of conventions.

1 A **poor** poster does not focus on early and modern farming methods, or the information it presents is generally inaccurate.

0 An **unscorable** poster is unreadable, is not presented as a poster, or has nothing to do with farming methods.

Performance Assessment

Chapter 5: Writing Comparisons

Goal

The student will compare and contrast the governments and rulers of ancient Assyria and Babylon.

Suggestions:

1. Review Lesson 2 and have students discuss similarities and differences between the governments of ancient Assyria and Babylon.

2. Model the process by constructing a comparison/contrast chart of the two civilizations.

Portfolio Opportunities

Have students evaluate their own comparisons by completing self-assessment forms. Then have students place their comparisons and self-assessments in their portfolios.

SCORING RUBRIC

4 An **excellent** comparison has a clear statement of comparison between life in ancient Babylon and Assyria. It includes at least two statements of comparison and at least two statements of contrast. Information is presented in a logical order, and each point is clearly defined as a comparison or a contrast. Examples: The empire of Assyria had its roots in northern Mesopotamia. It shared traditions of religion and writing with Babylonia, an empire based in southern Mesopotamia. Although Assyrians spoke a different language than the Babylonians, both used cuneiform to write. The city of Babylon and the city of Nineveh in Assyria were both walled, and both contained palaces and many temples. Ziggurats rose from Assyrian cities as they did from Babylon. The Assyrians used aqueducts to bring water to Nineveh from many miles away. The Babylonians built dams to control the flood waters of the Euphrates.

3 A **good** comparison has a clear statement of comparison between life in ancient Babylon and Assyria. It includes one or two statements of comparison and one or two statements of contrast. Information is presented in a logical order, and each point is clearly defined as a comparison or a contrast. The comparison is written with generally correct use of conventions.

2 A **fair** comparison has a statement of comparison between the government and rulers of ancient Babylon and those of Assyria. It includes one statement of comparison and one statement of contrast. Information may not be presented in a logical order, and the paragraph may include some inaccurate information. The comparison may include some errors in the use of conventions.

1 A **poor** comparison does not present a specific comparison or contrast between the two civilizations, or it presents generally inaccurate information.

0 An **unscorable** paragraph is incomplete or is not related to ancient Assyria and Babylon.

Performance Assessment

Chapter 5: Writing an Explanation

Goal

The student explains the Code of Hammurabi and the Ten Commandments and why they are regarded as important steps forward in civilization.

Suggestions:

1. Review Lessons 2 and 3 and have students discuss the Code of Hammurabi and the Ten Commandments and why they were important.

2. Model the process by giving an example of a lawbreaker, such as a thief, and discussing what might have happened to the lawbreaker under each code of laws.

Portfolio Opportunities

Have students exchange explanations with their partners and evaluate the explanations by completing peer assessment forms. Then have students place their explanations in their portfolios with the peer assessments.

SCORING RUBRIC

4 An **excellent** explanation has a main idea or topic sentence and at least three supporting paragraphs, and it presents information in a logical order. It explains the Code of Hammurabi and the Ten Commandments, and it gives at least two reasons explaining why they were important steps forward in civilization. Example: The Code of Hammurabi was a set of more than 200 laws which were applied to everyone under a government. It was important because it established standard laws, represented a system of justice, and made everyone answerable to both the government and to his or her fellow citizens. The Ten Commandments included ten statements that established standards of behavior applicable to everyone. They were important because they united the Hebrews under one god and forbade the worship of any other god. They also established a "higher" code of law by making people answerable to God and not to one another. The explanation is written with correct use of conventions (grammar, punctuation, capitalization, and spelling).

3 A **good** explanation has a main idea or topic sentence and two or three supporting paragraphs, and it presents information in a logical order. It explains the Code of Hammurabi and the Ten Commandments, and it gives one or two reasons explaining why they were important steps forward in civilization. The explanation is written with generally correct use of conventions.

2 A **fair** explanation describes the Code of Hammurabi and the Ten Commandments, and it gives one or two reasons explaining why they were important steps forward in civilization. The explanation relates to the main idea, but the main idea may not be clearly stated. Information may not be presented in a logical order. The explanation may include some errors in the use of conventions.

1 A **poor** explanation does not reflect an accurate understanding of the Code of Hammurabi and the Ten Commandments or their importance.

0 An **unscorable** explanation is incomplete or does not relate to the task.

Performance Assessment

Chapter 5: Writing Biographical Paragraphs

Goal

The student will write a brief biography of two of the following people: Sargon, Hammurabi, Abraham, Moses.

Suggestions:

1. Have students review Lessons 2 and 3 and discuss important facts about each of these four people.

2. Model the process by reading a brief biography or encyclopedia article about a notable person of the times, such as a pharaoh.

Portfolio Opportunities

Have students evaluate their own biographical paragraphs by telling what they like best about them. Then have students place their biographies and brief critiques in their portfolios.

<table>
<tr><td colspan="2" align="center">**SCORING RUBRIC**</td></tr>
<tr><td>4</td><td>An **excellent** biography includes one paragraph about each of two people: Sargon, Hammurabi, Abraham, or Moses. Each biographical paragraph provides at least three specific factual details about the person and at least two important events in which the person was involved, and it presents information in a logical order. Example: Sargon was the king of the city-state of Kish. He rose to power in about 2300 B.C. and united most of Mesopotamia in one empire. He conducted trade with the Phoenicians and the Egyptians, and he used cuneiform to conduct administrative aspects of his government throughout the empire. Sargon's empire lasted until about 2279 B.C. when the city-states rebelled against the empire. The paragraphs are written with correct use of conventions (grammar, punctuation, capitalization, and spelling).</td></tr>
<tr><td>3</td><td>A **good** biography includes one paragraph about each of two people: Sargon, Hammurabi, Abraham, or Moses. Each biographical paragraph provides two or three specific factual details about the person and at least one important event in which the person was involved, and it presents information in a logical order. The paragraphs are written with generally correct use of conventions.</td></tr>
<tr><td>2</td><td>A **fair** biography includes one paragraph about each of two people: Sargon, Hammurabi, Abraham, or Moses. Each biographical paragraph provides two specific factual details about the person and one important event in which the person was involved, although it may not present information in a logical order. The paragraphs may include some errors in the use of conventions.</td></tr>
<tr><td>1</td><td>A **poor** biography describes only one person, or it gives inaccurate information.</td></tr>
<tr><td>0</td><td>An **unscorable** biography is unreadable or does not relate to the task.</td></tr>
</table>

Performance Assessment

Chapter 6: Writing a List

Goal

The student will make a list of things about ancient Egypt that mark it as an important civilization.

Suggestions:

1. Have students review Lessons 2 and 3 and brainstorm a list of achievements of ancient Egypt.
2. Model the process by giving examples of things that made other civilizations important.

Portfolio Opportunities

Have students exchange lists with partners and evaluate the lists by completing peer assessment forms. Then have students display their lists or place them in their portfolios with peer assessment forms included.

SCORING RUBRIC

4   An **excellent** list includes at least four things about ancient Egypt that mark it as an important civilization. Items on the list are clearly numbered, bulleted, or delineated in some other way. Examples: Ancient Egypt developed a strong central government, it developed and used hieroglyphics for communicating over long distances, it created splendid monuments such as the Great Pyramid, it became the largest empire in the world at the time by conquering neighboring regions, it developed and spread knowledge of medicine, math, science, and numerous technologies such as metalworking. The list is written with correct use of conventions (grammar, punctuation, capitalization, and spelling).

3   A **good** list includes three things about ancient Egypt that mark it as an important civilization. Items on the list are clearly numbered, bulleted, or delineated in some other way. The list is written with generally correct use of conventions.

2   A **fair** list includes two things about ancient Egypt that mark it as an important civilization. Items on the list may not be clearly delineated, or it may include some inaccurate information. The list may include some errors in the use of conventions.

1   A **poor** list does not include things about ancient Egypt that mark it as an important civilization, or it presents generally inaccurate information.

0   An **unscorable** list is incomplete, is not presented as a list, or does not relate to ancient Egypt.

Performance Assessment

Chapter 6: Writing an Explanation

Goal

The student explains the structure of Egyptian society and how it was similar to the shape of a pyramid.

Suggestions:

1. Review Lesson 4 and have students discuss the levels of Egyptian society.

2. Model the process by reviewing the picture of the "social pyramid" on page 157.

Portfolio Opportunities

Have students exchange explanations with their partners and evaluate the explanations by telling what is good about the partner's explanation and what might be improved. Then have students place their explanations in their portfolios with the partner's comments included.

SCORING RUBRIC

4 An **excellent** explanation has a main idea or topic sentence and at least three supporting detail sentences, and it presents information in a logical order. It explains how the shape of Egyptian society was similar to that of a pyramid and describes at least four groups that made up the pyramid. Examples: The shape of Egyptian society was similar to that of a pyramid because there was a single leader, the pharaoh, at the highest point, and the groups below the pharaoh got larger as they descended. The largest groups, which had the least power, made up the base of the pyramid. The group below the pharaoh in rank was made up of government officials and nobles (such as Syrian princes). Further down the pyramid were craftworkers and artisans, followed by farmers. At the bottom were prisoners who had been turned into slaves. The explanation is written with correct use of conventions (grammar, punctuation, capitalization, and spelling).

3 A **good** explanation has a main idea or topic sentence and three supporting detail sentences, and it presents information in a logical order. It explains how the shape of Egyptian society was similar to that of a pyramid and describes three or four groups that made up the pyramid. Examples: The description of different groups may not include as much detail as it could. The explanation is written with generally correct use of conventions.

2 A **fair** explanation tells how the shape of Egyptian society was similar to that of a pyramid and describes two or three groups that made up the pyramid. The explanation relates to the main idea, but the main idea may not be clearly stated. Details may not be presented in a logical order. The explanation may include some errors in the use of conventions.

1 A **poor** explanation does not reflect an accurate understanding of the structure of Egyptian society.

0 An **unscorable** explanation is incomplete or does not relate to the task.

Performance Assessment

Chapter 6: Writing a Paragraph of Analysis

Goal
The student analyzes the effects of the Nile River on ancient Egyptian civilization in a written paragraph.

Suggestions:
1. Review Lesson 1 and have students discuss the effects of the Nile River on ancient Egyptian civilization.

2. Model the process by giving an example of one effect of the Nile River.

Portfolio Opportunities
Have students exchange analyses with their partners and evaluate the analyses by telling what is good about the partner's analysis and what might be improved. Then have students place their analyses in their portfolios with the partner's comments included.

SCORING RUBRIC

4 An **excellent** analysis has a main idea or topic sentence and at least three supporting detail sentences. It explains at least four effects of the Nile River on ancient Egyptian civilization, both positive and negative, and presents information in a logical order. Examples: The Nile River flooded the region with water and mud for four months of the year; in some years heavy floods washed away villages and livestock; the river deposited silt which made the land fertile for farming; it enabled farmers to irrigate farmland; it provided a means of transportation for moving goods and people from place to place. The analysis is written with correct use of conventions (grammar, punctuation, capitalization, and spelling).

3 A **good** analysis has a main idea or topic sentence and three supporting detail sentences. It explains three effects of the Nile River on ancient Egyptian civilization and presents information in a logical order. The analysis is written with generally correct use of conventions.

2 A **fair** analysis explains two effects of the Nile River on ancient Egyptian civilization. The analysis relates to the main idea, but the main idea may not be clearly stated. Details may not be presented in a logical order. The analysis may include some errors in the use of conventions.

1 A **poor** analysis does not reflect an accurate understanding of the effects of the Nile River on ancient Egyptian civilization.

0 An **unscorable** analysis is incomplete or does not relate to the task.

Performance Assessment

Chapter 7: Writing a Description

Goal
The student will write a paragraph describing the Nile.

Suggestions:
1. Have students review the relevant part of Lesson 1 and look at the map on page 167.
2. Model the process by describing another region in Africa.

Portfolio Opportunities
Have students exchange descriptions with their partners and evaluate the descriptions by completing peer assessment forms. Then have students display their descriptions or place them in their portfolios with the peer assessment forms.

SCORING RUBRIC

4 An **excellent** description clearly describes the Nile and the effects of it flooding the river valley and the people who live there. Information is presented in a logical order. Five detailed characteristics of the river itself are given. These may include the route of the Nile and the Blue and White Niles, the source, length, direction in which the rivers flow, and that the Nile empties into the Mediterranean sea. The cataracts are also mentioned. The description also details how the flooding affected the people of the valley. Information may include: floodwaters carried silt to the Nile's riverbanks. People could farm the flood plains, growing wheat, barley, peas, lentils, and grasses. The bones of domestic animals have also been found there. The description is written with correct use of conventions (grammar, punctuation, capitalization, and spelling).

3 A **good** description clearly describes the Nile and lists four characteristics of it. Information is presented in a logical order. The paragraph includes a description of the effects of flooding on the river valley and the people who lived there. The description is written with generally correct use of conventions.

2 A **fair** description describes the Nile and lists three important characteristics of it. It gives a basic description of the effects of flooding on the river valley and the people who live there. Information may not be presented in a logical order, or the paragraph may include inaccurate information. The description may include some errors in the use of conventions.

1 A **poor** description describes only one or two characteristics of the Nile, or it presents inaccurate information.

0 An **unscorable** description is unreadable or does not relate to the Nile.

Performance Assessment

Chapter 7: Writing a Summary

Goal

The student will write a paragraph summarizing the most important events in the history of the kingdom of Kush.

Suggestions:

1. Have students review Lesson 2 and discuss the history of the kingdom of Kush.

2. Model the process by writing and reading a summary of the Nok culture.

Portfolio Opportunities

Have students exchange summaries with their partners and evaluate the summaries by writing one or two sentences telling what is good about the summary and what might be improved. Then have students display their summaries or place them in their portfolios with the partner's comments.

SCORING RUBRIC

4 An **excellent** summary clearly describes at least five important aspects of Kush's history. The summary has a main idea or topic sentence and at least three supporting detail sentences, and it presents information in a logical order. The summary is written with correct use of conventions (grammar, punctuation, capitalization, and spelling).

3 A **good** summary clearly describes four important aspects of Kush's history. The summary has a main idea or topic sentence and at least two supporting detail sentences, and it presents information in a logical order. The summary is written with generally correct use of conventions.

2 A **fair** summary clearly describes three important aspects of Kush's history. The summary has a main idea or topic sentence, but it may not be written clearly. Details may not be presented in a logical order, or the summary may include some inaccurate information. The summary may include some errors in the use of conventions.

1 A **poor** summary describes only one or two aspects of Kush's history, or it presents inaccurate information.

0 An **unscorable** summary is unreadable or is not related to Kush's history.

Performance Assessment

Chapter 7: Writing a Catalog Entry

Goal

The student will, as the owner of a store that sells ancient artifacts, write a paragraph for his or her catalog describing a Nok figurine.

Suggestions:

1. Have students review Lesson 3 and study the photographs of Nok figurines.

2. Model the process by reading a description from a catalog.

Portfolio Opportunities

Have students exchange paragraphs with their partners and have the partner tell what is good about the paragraph and what might be improved. Then have students read their catalog entries to the class and place them in their portfolios.

SCORING RUBRIC

4 An **excellent** catalog entry describes the Nok figuring accurately, and in detail. It uses visual language and refers to the history of the Nok. Information is presented in a logical order and a catalog number and price may be included. The catalog entry is written with correct use of conventions (grammar, punctuation, capitalization, and spelling).

3 A **good** catalog entry accurately describes the Nok figurine. It uses visual language and mentions the history of the Nok. Information is presented in a logical order and a catalog number and price may be included. The catalog entry is written with generally correct use of conventions.

2 A **fair** catalog entry describes the Nok figurine. It uses visual language but may not present information in a logical order and does not mention the history of the Nok. The catalog entry may include some errors in the use of conventions.

1 A **poor** catalog entry does not accurately describe the Nok figurine or does not mention the history of the Nok.

0 An **unscorable** catalog entry is unreadable or does not relate to the task.

Performance Assessment

Unit 3 Project: Comparing Then and Now

Goal

The student will develop a poster comparing a civilization and its river in ancient times and today.

Suggestions:

1. Have students brainstorm a list of rivers and ancient civilizations in the unit and discuss ways to find information about how the rivers affect civilizations today.

2. Model the process by giving an example description of a large city on a well-known river, such as the Nile.

Portfolio Opportunities

Have students work with small groups or exchange their posters with partners and evaluate the posters by completing peer assessment forms. Then have students display their posters and place the peer assessment forms in their portfolios.

SCORING RUBRIC

4 An **excellent** poster focuses on a river that was important to an ancient civilization (such as the Nile, Euphrates, or Tigris) and compares the civilization and its river then and now. The comparison includes a paragraph explaining at least four aspects of life affected by the river, such as the jobs people have, foods they eat, forms of transportation, and houses they live in. The poster reflects the results of research, and it includes pictures and accurate descriptions of the civilization and its river. The poster is presented in a colorful and creative way, and the text is written with correct use of conventions (grammar, punctuation, capitalization, and spelling).

3 A **good** poster focuses on a river that was important to an ancient civilization and compares the civilization and its river then and now. The comparison includes a paragraph explaining three aspects of life affected by the river, such as the jobs people have, foods they eat, forms of transportation, and houses they live in. The poster reflects the results of research, and it includes pictures and accurate descriptions of the civilization and its river. The poster is presented in a somewhat creative way, and the text is written with generally correct use of conventions.

2 A **fair** poster focuses on a river that was important to an ancient civilization and compares the civilization and its river then and now. The comparison includes a paragraph explaining two or three aspects of life affected by the river. The poster may not reflect the results of research, and some of the descriptions may not be completely accurate. The text may include some errors in the use of conventions.

1 A **poor** poster does not focus on a river civilization, does not compare the civilization then and now, or gives generally inaccurate information.

0 An **unscorable** poster is incomplete, is not presented as a poster, or has nothing to do with a river and its civilization.

Performance Assessment

Chapter 8: Writing a Letter

Goal

The student will, as one of the archaeologists who had uncovered the remains of Mohenjo-Daro, writes a letter to a friend describing the most interesting artifacts found there, and what they reveal about the lives of the people who lived there.

Suggestions:

1. Review Lesson 2 and have students discuss what artifacts were discovered at Mohenjo-Daro.

2. Model the process by telling students what some of today's everyday items might reveal about today's way of life.

Portfolio Opportunities

Have students exchange letters and evaluate the letters by completing peer assessment forms. Then have students place their letters and peer assessments in their portfolios.

SCORING RUBRIC

4 An **excellent** letter clearly describes at least five major artifacts found at Mohenjo-Daro. The letter is addressed to a friend and is written from the perspective of an archeologist working at Mohenjo-Daro. It presents information in a logical order. It describes artifacts accurately and includes a detailed explanation of what they reveal about the people who lived in Mohenjo-Daro. For example, beautiful figures carved into small stone squares were probably used for marking belongings. Necklaces made from stone found in present-day India show that the people of Mohenjo-Daro traded. The letter also includes descriptions of the buildings and layout of the city. For example, the bath may have had religious importance and the planning of the town, shown by the use of same-size bricks and a sewer system, suggest that Mohenjo-Daro had a strong government. The letter is written with correct use of conventions (grammar, punctuation, capitalization, and spelling).

3 A **good** letter clearly describes four major artifacts found at Mohenjo-Daro. The letter is addressed to a friend and is written from the perspective of an archeologist working at Mohenjo-Daro. It presents information in a logical order. It describes artifacts accurately and includes an explanation of what they reveal about the people who lived in Mohenjo-Daro. The letter is written with generally correct use of conventions.

2 A **fair** letter describes three major artifacts found at Mohenjo-Daro. It may not present information in a logical order, or may include inaccurate information. The letter may not say how the artifacts reveal information about the people who lived in Mohenjo-Daro. It may include some errors in the use of conventions.

1 A **poor** letter does not describe artifacts found at Mohenjo-Daro, or presents generally inaccurate information.

0 An **unscorable** letter is incomplete or is not related to the subject.

Performance Assessment

Chapter 8: Writing a Report

Goal

The student will write a class report on the Hindu belief in a constant cycle of birth, death, and rebirth and how this belief affects the way Hindus live.

Suggestions:

1. Review Lesson 3 and have students discuss the principles of Hinduism.

2. Model the process by giving an example of a Hindu belief and how it affects the way people live.

Portfolio Opportunities

Have students evaluate their own reports by telling what they like best about them and what might be improved. Then have students place their reports and brief critiques in their portfolios.

SCORING RUBRIC

4 An **excellent** report clearly explains the Hindu belief in reincarnation and gives at least three examples of how this belief affects the way Hindus live. The report clearly states the topic in a main idea or topic sentence and presents information in a logical order. Example: According to the Vedas, people move in a constant cycle of life, death, and rebirth. This cycle is called reincarnation. Everyone is born into a certain caste, and one's caste determines how that person will live. Members of each caste followed the dharma, or laws and duties, of their caste. For example, a person born into the servant caste was destined to serve those in other castes, and part of the dharma of the servants was to do their jobs cheerfully. Bad deeds done in one lifetime must be paid for in another, so a person who has done bad deeds may return in the next life as a servant. Priests are people who have done good deeds in past lives. The report is written with correct use of conventions (grammar, punctuation, capitalization, and spelling).

3 A **good** report explains the Hindu belief in reincarnation and gives two examples of how this belief affects the way Hindus live. The report clearly states the topic in a main idea or topic sentence and presents information in a logical order. The report is written with generally correct use of conventions.

2 A **fair** report explains the Hindu belief in reincarnation and gives an example of how this belief affects the way Hindus live. The report relates to the topic, but the topic may not be clearly stated. Information may not be presented in a logical order. The paragraph may include some errors in the use of conventions.

1 A **poor** report does not explain the Hindu belief in reincarnation or how this belief affects the way Hindus live.

0 An **unscorable** report is unreadable or does not relate to the task.

Performance Assessment

Chapter 8: Writing an Essay

Goal

The student explains India's caste system and the beliefs that created it by writing an essay.

Suggestions:

1. Review Lesson 3 and have students discuss the principles of the caste system.

2. Model the process by bringing in and sharing an essay or article on a similar topic concerning the people of the United States.

Portfolio Opportunities

Have students exchange essays with their partners and evaluate the essays by completing peer assessment forms. Then have students collect their essays in a notebook or place them in their portfolios with the peer assessments.

SCORING RUBRIC

4 An **excellent** essay describes the four classes of people in India's caste system, the beliefs that created the caste system, and how it is changing. The essay has a clearly stated main idea, topic, or thesis, and it presents supporting details in a logical order. For example, the essay describes how four different classes of humans were created from a god's body: priests, princes, professionals and merchants, and servants. Everyone was born into a certain caste, and one's caste determined how that person would live. Members of each caste followed the dharma, or laws and duties, of their caste. Someone who violated the rules of the caste were forced to live outside all castes with few rights, and their children became "untouchables." The Indian caste system has changed in recent years. For example, in 1950 the Indian government made it illegal to mistreat or show disrespect for Hindu "outcastes." The essay is written with correct use of conventions (grammar, punctuation, capitalization, and spelling).

3 A **good** essay describes the four classes of people in India's caste system, the beliefs that created the caste system, and how it is changing. The essay has a clearly stated main idea, topic, or thesis, and it presents supporting details in a logical order. The description of the beliefs that created the system may not be as complete as it could be. The essay is written with generally correct use of conventions.

2 A **fair** essay describes the four classes of people in India's caste system and the beliefs that created the caste system, but it may not describe "outcastes" or how the caste system is changing. The essay has a main idea, topic, or thesis, but it may not be clearly stated. Details may not be presented in a logical order, or some of the information may be inaccurate. The essay may include some errors in the use of conventions.

1 A **poor** essay does not reflect an accurate understanding of India's caste system.

0 An **unscorable** essay is incomplete or does not relate to the subject of India's caste system.

Performance Assessment

Chapter 9: Writing a Journal

Goal
The student will describe life as a student in the Grand School in the time of the Han Dynasty by writing a journal entry.

Suggestions:
1. Review Lesson 4 and have students discuss what they might have seen and experienced in the Grand School in the time of the Han Dynasty.

2. Model the process by writing your own journal entry as a teacher in the Grand School.

Portfolio Opportunities
Have students exchange journal entries with partners and write a sentence describing what they like best about the partner's journal entry. Then have students display their journal entries or place them in their portfolios with partners' comments included.

SCORING RUBRIC

4 An **excellent** journal entry gives specific details about the studies and the year-end test in the Grand School in the time of the Han Dynasty. It is written from the perspective of a student in the school and includes at least five personal observations about the studies and about the long test at the end of the year. For example, the journal entry might describe what the student studied: China's poetry, history, proper behavior, and folk songs. It might describe aspects of Confucianism, such as the need to have respect within the family and respect for the ruler of the country. It might describe the long test students had to take after a year of study and the results of passing the test: earning jobs as government officials or as teachers in province schools, and winning great respect in society for being well educated. The journal entry is written with correct use of conventions (grammar, punctuation, capitalization, and spelling).

3 A **good** journal entry gives specific details about the studies and the year-end test in the Grand School in the time of the Han Dynasty. It is written from the perspective of a student in the school and includes four personal observations about the studies and about the long test at the end of the year. The journal entry is written with generally correct use of conventions.

2 A **fair** journal entry gives specific details about the studies and the year-end test in the Grand School in the time of the Han Dynasty. It is written from the perspective of a student in the school and includes three personal observations about the studies and about the long test at the end of the year. The journal entry may include some inaccurate information and some errors in the use of conventions.

1 A **poor** journal entry does not include specific details about life in the Grand School or presents generally inaccurate information.

0 An **unscorable** journal entry is incomplete, is not presented as a journal, or does not relate to the Grand School in the time of the Han Dynasty.

Performance Assessment

Chapter 9: Writing an Article

Goal

The student will describe ancient Chinese civilization and the contributions it has made to world cultures in an article for a school newspaper.

Suggestions:

1. Review the information in Lessons 2, 3, and 4 andhave students brainstorm a list of Chinese achievements.

2. Model the process by bringing in and sharing an article, preferably from a school newspaper, about a historical topic.

Portfolio Opportunities

Have students evaluate their own articles by completing self-assessment forms. Then have students share their articles with the class and place the self-assessments in their portfolios.

SCORING RUBRIC

4 An **excellent** article tells who, what, when, where, and why in a logical order with correct use of conventions (grammar, punctuation, capitalization, and spelling). It describes at least six contributions of Chinese civilization and attributes them to the correct dynasty. Examples: The Shang Dynasty began about 1700 B.C. and lasted about 600 years. Its most notable achievement was the development of a system of writing. The Qin Dynasty came to power around 221 B.C. and lasted about fifteen years. Among the achievements during this dynasty were a centralized system of government, a standard system of writing, and a system of money. The Han Dynasty began around 206 B.C. Among its achievements were the application of the principles of Confucianism in government and education, the invention of paper, and remarkable advances in mathematics, science (astronomy, the use of seismographs, discovery of new medicines), and arts (creation of the first Chinese dictionary).

3 A **good** article reflects three or four of the 5 Ws in a logical order with generally correct use of conventions. It describes four or five contributions of Chinese civilization and attributes them to the correct dynasty.

2 A **fair** article reflects two or three of the 5 Ws. It describes three or four contributions of Chinese civilization. It may not present information in a logical order, or it may include some inaccurate information. The article may include some errors in the use of conventions.

1 A **poor** article may describe Chinese achievements in a general way, but it does not describe when, who, or where.

0 An **unscorable** article is unreadable or has nothing to do with Chinese achievements.

Performance Assessment

Chapter 9: Writing About Perspectives

Goal
The student, as a student living in ancient China, will write three paragraphs about the Huang River.

Suggestions:
1. Review Lesson 1 and have students discuss some of their impressions of the Huang River.

2. Model the process by giving an example of a fact about or an impression of the Huang River.

Portfolio Opportunities
Have students exchange papers with their partners and evaluate the papers by completing peer assessment forms. Then have students place their papers and peer assessments in their portfolios.

SCORING RUBRIC

4 An **excellent** paper has a composition of three or more paragraphs about the Huang River. It includes at least three facts about the river, at least two observations or impressions about it, and a sense of its importance throughout Chinese history. Each paragraph has a clear main idea or topic sentence and presents details in a logical order. Examples: The Huang River begins in the Himalayas and flows 3,000 miles across northern China. It creates miles of soggy but fertile marshland, and the first farming communities in China developed along this river around 4000 B.C. During the summer huge amounts of loess are washed into the river and carried downstream as silt. The yellow color of loess gives the river its name. The loess creates good farmland, but it is so fine that it sometimes is blown away. For many centuries history has proven that "whoever controls the Huang River controls China." The composition is written with correct use of conventions (grammar, punctuation, capitalization, and spelling).

3 A **good** paper has a composition of three paragraphs about the Huang River. It includes three facts about the river, one or two observations or impressions about it, and a sense of its importance throughout Chinese history. Each paragraph has a clear main idea or topic sentence and presents information in a logical order. The composition is written with generally correct use of conventions.

2 A **fair** paper has a composition of two or three paragraphs about the Huang River. It includes two facts about the river, an observation or impression about it, and a sense of its importance throughout Chinese history. Each paragraph has a main idea or topic, although it may not be clearly stated. It may not present information in a logical order, and the composition may include some errors in the use of conventions.

1 A **poor** paper has only one paragraph about the Huang River or presents generally inaccurate information.

0 An **unscorable** paper is incomplete or is not related to the task.

Performance Assessment

Chapter 10: Writing a Description

Goal

The student will write a paragraph describing the land, climate, and early people of Middle America.

Suggestions:

1. Have students review Lesson 1 and discuss the environment of Middle America.

2. Model the process by describing one aspect of Middle America.

Portfolio Opportunities

Have students exchange descriptions with their partners and evaluate the descriptions by writing a sentence telling what is best about the description. Then have students display their descriptions or place them in their portfolios with the partner's comments.

SCORING RUBRIC

4 An **excellent** description describes at least five aspects of Middle America. The paragraph has a main idea or topic sentence and at least three supporting detail sentences, it used visual language, and it presents information in a logical order. Examples: Middle America covered parts of what is now Mexico and Central America. It has steep mountains and rain forest. There is a large area of rolling hills called the Central Plateau in the northern part of the region, and the valleys there contain ancient volcanoes. After the Ice Age, a wide variety of plants and animals lived there. Most of Middle America is in the tropical zone, near the equator. The climate varies due to the mountains. Most of the region's rain falls between May and October. Evidence of people living there dates back 11,000 years. It is believed that these people gathered wild onions, squash, avocados, and hunted rabbits and deer. The description is written with correct use of conventions (grammar, punctuation, capitalization, and spelling).

3 A **good** description describes four aspects of Middle America. The paragraph has a main idea or topic sentence and three supporting detail sentences, it uses visual language, and it presents information in a logical order. The description is written with generally correct use of conventions.

2 A **fair** description describes two or three aspects of Middle America. The paragraph has a main idea or topic sentence, but it may not be written clearly. Details may not be presented in a logical order, or the paragraph may include some inaccurate information. The description may include some errors in the use of conventions.

1 A **poor** description describes only one aspect of Middle America, or it presents generally inaccurate information.

0 An **unscorable** description is unreadable or is not related to Middle America.

Performance Assessment

Chapter 10: Writing a Journal Entry

Goal

The student, as a resident of La Venta 3,000 years ago, will write a journal entry about his or her life there.

Suggestions:

1. Review Lesson 2 and have students discuss what they might have seen and experienced in La Venta.
2. Model the process by writing your own journal entry.

Portfolio Opportunities

Have students exchange journal entries with partners and write a sentence describing what they like best about the partner's journal entry. Then have students display their journal entries or place them in their portfolios with partners' comments included.

SCORING RUBRIC

4 An **excellent** journal entry gives specific details about life in La Venta 3,000 years ago. The journal entry notes a specific day or date and includes at least five personal observations about life in the ancient city. It includes a description of La Venta's location; that it was on a large island surrounded by swamps and rivers. Examples of what the journal entry might note include the following. La Venta had a large mound and several smaller ones. It had a large plaza surrounded by stone pillars and four huge stone heads each with its own helmet and symbol. Stone carvers lived in La Venta making statues, tools for grinding corn, or more delicate objects. Most people were farmers, and the leaders controlled the farmland. They also built stone monuments. The Olmec who lived in La Venta practiced polytheism and made sacrifices on their altars. The jaguar was believed to be the most powerful animal and its image was found in carvings and on a mosaic. Simple, light clothing and beautiful jewelry was worn. Rubber balls were made for games and musical instruments for entertainment. The journal entry is written with correct use of conventions (grammar, punctuation, capitalization, and spelling).

3 A **good** journal entry gives specific details about life in La Venta 3,000 years ago. The journal entry notes a specific day or date and includes three or four personal observations about life in the ancient city. The journal entry is written with generally correct use of conventions.

2 A **fair** journal entry gives some details about life in La Venta 3,000 years ago. The journal entry includes two or three personal observations about life in the ancient city. The journal entry may include some inaccurate information and some errors in the use of conventions.

1 A **poor** journal entry does not include specific details about life in La Venta 3,000 years ago, or it presents generally inaccurate information.

0 An **unscorable** journal entry is incomplete, is not presented as a journal, or does not relate to La Venta.

Performance Assessment

Chapter 10: Writing Interview Questions

Goal
The student writes a series of interview questions for one of the ancient people who helped build a mound.

Suggestions:
1. Review Lesson 3 and discuss the kinds of questions one might ask one of the ancient people who helped build a mound.

2. Model the process by playing the role of one of the ancient mound-builders and having students ask you questions.

Portfolio Opportunities
Have students evaluate their own interviews by using them to role play with partners and discussing what is good about them and what might be improved. Then have students share their interviews with the class and place the interviews in their portfolios.

SCORING RUBRIC

4 An **excellent** series of interview questions has at least five questions that are easy to understand, are specific to the ancient mound-builders, lead to informative responses, and are presented in logical sequence. Questions will ask what the purpose of the mound was, specifying the theories that they were used for burial, religious ceremonies, meeting places for festivals, or for astronomy. The questions will also ask why a mound was shaped in a particular way, and how the mound was built, asking, for example, how long it took, how many people worked on it, or who made the baskets for carrying the earth. The interview questions are written with correct use of conventions (grammar, punctuation, capitalization, and spelling).

3 A **good** series of interview questions has three or four well-written questions that are easy to understand, are specific to the ancient mound-builders, lead to informative responses, and are presented in a logical order. The interview questions are written with generally correct use of conventions.

2 A **fair** series of interview questions has two or three well-written questions that are easy to understand, are specific to the ancient mound-builders, and lead to informative responses. The questions may not be presented in a logical sequence, or they may include questions that are not appropriate to the topic. The interview questions may include some inaccurate information, or some errors in the use of conventions.

1 A **poor** series of interview questions does not have clear, focused questions, and does not lead to informative responses.

0 An **unscorable** series of interview questions is unreadable, is not written as an interview, or does not have anything to do with the mound builders.

Performance Assessment

Unit 4 Project: Make a Building

Goal

The student will write a report about the building styles of a culture in the unit and create a model building.

Suggestions:

1. Have students brainstorm a list of cultures covered in the unit and discuss ways to find more information about a culture's building styles.

2. Model the process by showing students a picture of a building created by one of the cultures in the unit.

Portfolio Opportunities

Have students present their reports and buildings to the class and evaluate the projects by completing peer assessment forms. Then have students display their buildings and place the peer assessment forms in their portfolios.

SCORING RUBRIC

4 An **excellent** project includes a report about the building styles in a culture covered in the unit and a model building representing the style. The report has a clearly stated main idea or topic and two or three supporting paragraphs. It reflects the results of research and presents information in a logical order. The report is written with correct use of conventions (grammar, punctuation, capitalization, and spelling). The model building is well constructed and accurately reflects the building style of the given culture.

3 A **good** project includes a report about the building styles in a culture covered in the unit and a model building representing the style. The report has a clearly stated main idea or topic and one or two supporting paragraphs. It reflects the results of research and presents information in a logical order. The report is written with generally correct use of conventions. The model building is fairly well constructed and accurately reflects the building style of the given culture.

2 A **fair** project includes a report about the building styles in a culture covered in the unit and a model building representing the style. The report has a main idea or topic, although it may not be clearly stated, and at least three supporting information sentences. It reflects the results of some research, but it may not present information in a logical order. The report may include some errors in the use of conventions. The model building generally reflects the building style of the given culture, although it may have some inaccurate details.

1 A **poor** project does not include a report or does not include a model building, it reflects no results of research, or it gives generally inaccurate information.

0 An **unscorable** project is incomplete or has nothing to do with the building styles of a culture in the unit.

Performance Assessment

Chapter 11: Writing an Explanation

Goal
The student will describe the land of Canaan and explain why the Hebrews went there.

Suggestions:
1. Review Lessons 1 and 2 and have students discuss the geography of ancient Canaan and why Abraham and Sarah went there.

2. Model the process by describing the climate of ancient Canaan.

Portfolio Opportunities
Have students exchange explanations with their partners and evaluate the explanations by telling what is good about the partner's explanation and what might be improved. Then have students place their explanations in their portfolios with the partner's comments attached.

SCORING RUBRIC

4 An **excellent** explanation has a main idea or topic sentence and at least three supporting detail sentences. It provides a comprehensive and detailed description of Canaan and offers a fact-based explanation of why the Hebrews went there. The paragraph should include the following details about Canaan: It was an area of marked contrasts, including green, well-watered areas, and dry, rocky desert. There were steep mountains and river valleys below sea level. Much of northern Canaan was a fertile land of trees and green fields, while the southern part of Canaan was dry and full of scrub, although oases provided relief from the harsh environment. The climate was varied, with weather ranging from snowy winters to desert heat. The Hebrews went to Canaan because, according to the Bible, God instructed Abraham to go there. The explanation is written with correct use of conventions (grammar, punctuation, capitalization, and spelling).

3 A **good** explanation has a main idea or topic sentence an three supporting detail sentences. It provides a description of Canaan, but may be lacking in one or two important details. It provides an explanation of why the Hebrews went there. The explanation is written with generally correct use of conventions.

2 A **fair** explanation describes the land of Canaan and states the reason for the Hebrews going there. The explanation relates to the main idea, but the main idea may not be clearly stated. Details may be absent from the description. The explanation may include some errors in the use of conventions.

1 A **poor** explanation does not offer a detailed description of Canaan and does not explicitly address the issue of why the Hebrews went there.

0 An **unscorable** explanation is incomplete or does not relate to the task.

Performance Assessment

Chapter 11: Writing Biographical Paragraphs

Goal

The student will write a paragraph about two of the following individuals: Abraham, Joshua, Deborah, King David.

Suggestions:

1. Review Lessons 2 and 3 and have students discuss the roles various individuals played in the history of Israel and the Hebrews.
2. Model the process by choosing another figure in the chapter, and describing his or her actions, role, or importance.

Portfolio Opportunities

Have students exchange paragraphs with their partners and evaluate their paragraphs by completing peer assessment forms. Then have students place their paragraphs in their portfolios with the partner's comments attached.

SCORING RUBRIC

4 An **excellent** paragraph provides a biographical sketch of each of the two individuals consisting of detailed information on the important events in which they were involved, the historical roles they played, their actions, and interesting details or characteristics about the individuals. Example: Joshua was a Hebrew military leader during the time when the Israelites were conquering Canaan. He led the Israelites in an attack on the city of Jericho and is said to have threatened anyone who tried to rebuild Jericho after his forces had destroyed it. He conquered many other cities in ancient Canaan. The paragraph is written with correct use of conventions (grammar, punctuation, capitalization, and spelling).

3 A **good** paragraph provides a biographical sketch of the two individuals consisting of information on the important events in which the individuals were involved, the historical roles they played, their actions, and interesting details or characteristics about them. The information on the two individuals may not be as detailed as it could be. The paragraph is written with generally correct use of conventions.

2 A **fair** paragraph provides a biographical sketch of the two individuals consisting of information on the important events in which they were involved, the historical roles they played, and their actions. The information is not very detailed and the paragraph does not include descriptions of any interesting characteristics for which the individuals may have been known. The paragraph includes some errors in the use of conventions.

1 A **poor** paragraph does not focus on the individual and presents inaccurate information.

0 An **unscorable** paragraph is incomplete or does not relate to the task.

Performance Assessment

Chapter 11: Writing an Interview

Goal
The student will write an interview with Moses.

Suggestions:
1. Review Lesson 2 and have students discuss the kinds of questions an interviewer might ask Moses.

2. Model the process by playing the role of Moses and having students ask you questions.

Portfolio Opportunities
Have students evaluate their own interviews by using them to role-play with partners and discussing what is good about them and what might be improved. Then have students share their interview with the class and place the interviews in their portfolios.

SCORING RUBRIC

4 An **excellent** interview has at least five well-written questions that are easy to understand, are specific to Moses and his experience, lead to informative responses, and are presented in a logical sequence. Questions might focus on Moses' early years as a member of the royal household in Egypt, the reasons for his fleeing from Egypt, his call from God to free the Israelites in Egypt, his leading of the Israelites out of Egypt, the wandering in the desert for forty years, his receiving of the law on Mount Sinai, and his final words to the Israelites before his death. The interview also provides reasonable responses to the questions from Moses' point of view. The questions and answers in the interview are clearly labeled, and the interview is written with correct use of conventions (grammar, punctuation, capitalization, and spelling).

3 A **good** interview has at least four well-written questions that are easy to understand, are specific to Moses and his experience, lead to informative responses, and are presented in a logical sequence. The interview also provides reasonable responses to the questions from Moses' point of view. The questions and answers in the interview are clearly labeled, and the interview is written with generally correct use of conventions.

2 A **fair** interview has at least two or three well-written questions that are easy to understand, are specific to Moses and his experience, and lead to informative responses. The questions may not be presented in a logical sequence, or they may not be appropriate to the topic. The interview also provides reasonable responses to the questions from Moses' point of view, although they may include some inaccurate information. The questions and answers in the interview may not be clearly labeled, and the interview may include some errors in the use of conventions.

1 A **poor** interview does not have clear, focused questions, and does not lead to informative responses.

0 An **unscorable** interview is not written as an interview or does not have anything to do with Moses and his experience.

Performance Assessment

Chapter 12: Writing About Contrasts

Goal

The student will write a paragraph describing the differences between Athens and Sparta.

Suggestions:

1. Review Lesson 3 and have students discuss the characteristics of Athens and Sparta and how they differed.

2. Model the process by giving an example of one way in which Athens and Sparta differed.

Portfolio Opportunities

Have students exchange paragraphs with their partners and evaluate the paragraphs by telling what is good about the partner's paragraph and what might be improved. Then have students place their paragraphs in their portfolios with the partner's comments attached.

SCORING RUBRIC

4 An **excellent** paragraph has a main idea or topic sentence and at least three supporting detail sentences. It provides a comprehensive description of Athens and Sparta, providing detailed information on the areas in which the two city-states differed. Examples: Sparta had more slaves than Athens. The leaders of Sparta dedicated more of their time to making Sparta the strongest military power in Greece, while the leaders of Athens spent less time and energy building a strong army. Spartan girls practiced sports, in order to be strong mothers of strong children, while girls in Athens did not practice sports but stayed at home to help their mothers. Boys in Sparta spent more time than boys in Athens preparing to be soldiers. The paragraph is written with correct use of conventions (grammar, punctuation, capitalization, and spelling).

3 A **good** paragraph has a main idea or topic sentence and at least three supporting detail sentences. It provides a description of Athens and Sparta, with detailed information on the areas in which the two city-states differed. The paragraph is written with generally correct use of conventions.

2 A **fair** paragraph describes the differences between Athens and Sparta, but may not include a clearly stated main idea. It may lack detail and one or two points may be inaccurate. The paragraph may include some errors in the use of conventions.

1 A **poor** paragraph presents generally inaccurate information about the differences between Athens and Sparta.

0 An **unscorable** paragraph is incomplete or does not relate to the topic.

Performance Assessment

Chapter 12: Writing a Paragraph

Goal

The student will write a paragraph from the point of view of a citizen of Tyre, on how life changed there after the Babylonians cut off the supply roads.

Suggestions:

1. Review Lesson 2 and have students discuss the circumstances of the Babylonian attack on the city of Tyre.

2. Model the process by reading an article on a similar situation in another time or place.

Portfolio Opportunities

Have students exchange paragraphs with their partners and evaluate the paragraphs by completing peer assessment forms. Then have students place their paragraphs in their portfolios with the peer assessment forms.

SCORING RUBRIC

4   An **excellent** paragraph provides a graphic, fact-based description of what life in Tyre would have been like after the Babylonians cut off the supply roads leading to the city. The paragraph makes clear the importance of the supply roads to Tyre, in that this island-based city received most of its water and food from trade. The paragraph is clearly written from the point of view of a citizen of ancient Tyre, and may mention a reluctance of the citizens to surrender. It is written with correct use of conventions (grammar, punctuation, capitalization, and spelling).

3   A **good** paragraph provides a fact-based description of what life in Tyre would have been like after the Babylonians cut off the supply roads leading to the city. The paragraph makes clear the importance of the supply roads to Tyre. The paragraph is clearly written from the point of view of a citizen of ancient Tyre, and with generally correct use of conventions.

2   A **fair** paragraph provides a description of what life in Tyre would have been like after the Babylonians cut off the supply roads leading to the city. The paragraph may include some inaccurate information, or it may not be clearly written from the point of view of a citizen of ancient Tyre. There may be some errors in the use of conventions.

1   A **poor** paragraph contains inaccurate information or is not written from the point of view of a citizen of ancient Tyre.

0   An **unscorable** paragraph is incomplete or does not relate to the task.

Performance Assessment

Chapter 12: Writing an Article

Goal
The student will write an article about the ancient Phoenicians, describing their contributions to world history.

Suggestions:
1. Review Lesson 2 and have students discuss the accomplishments of the ancient Phoenicians.

2. Model the process by describing one way the Phoenicians contributed to world history, such as the example they set of building colonies.

Portfolio Opportunities
Have students exchange articles with their partners and evaluate the article by telling what is good about the partner's article and what might be improved. Then have students share their articles with the class and place them in their portfolios with the partner's comments attached.

SCORING RUBRIC

4 An **excellent** article is clearly written with a lead paragraph followed by supporting paragraphs. The article provides comprehensive information about the ancient Phoenicians and their contributions to world history. Facts in the article include most of the following points: the Phoenicians were world traders, establishing trade routes in much of the Mediterranean world and possibly traveling as far as India, Arabia, and present-day Britain. The Phoenicians built colonies in a number of places, particularly around the western Mediterranean, and a few beyond the Strait of Gibraltar. Through the exchange of goods and ideas, the Phoenicians linked together many ancient civilizations, and their exploration was an example for later civilizations. They also introduced a system of writing based on an alphabet—a form still in use today. The article is written with correct use of conventions (grammar, punctuation, capitalization, and spelling).

3 A **good** article is clearly written with a lead paragraph followed by supporting paragraphs. The article provides information on many of the points about the ancient Phoenicians and their contributions to world history. The article is written with generally correct use of conventions.

2 A **fair** article provides information about the ancient Phoenicians and their contributions to world history, although it may not be written in the form of an article. Some of the information may be inaccurate or not presented in adequate detail. The article may include some errors in the use of conventions.

1 A **poor** article does not reflect an accurate understanding of the ancient Phoenicians and their contributions to world history.

0 An **unscorable** article is incomplete or does not relate to the task.

Performance Assessment

Chapter 13: Writing a Comparison

Goal

The student will write a paragraph comparing democracy in Athens and the United States.

Suggestions:

1. Review Lesson 2 and have students discuss how democracy was practiced in Athens and how it is practiced in the United States today.

2. Model the process by describing one aspect of the practice of democracy in Athens.

Portfolio Opportunities

Have students exchange paragraphs with their partners and evaluate the paragraphs by telling what is good about the partner's paragraph and what might be improved. Then have students place their paragraphs in their portfolios with the partner's comments.

SCORING RUBRIC

4 An **excellent** paragraph has a main idea or topic sentence and at least three or four supporting detail sentences. It presents a thorough, well-balanced comparison of the practice of democracy in ancient Athens and in the United States, listing areas in which the practice of democracy was similar and in which it was different. For example, in both Athens and the United States, citizens serve on juries and hold government jobs. While both Athenian citizens and citizens of the United States today help create laws, citizens in Athens voted directly in their government. In the United States, citizens elect representatives to vote for them. Athens had nothing quite like the executive branch of the United States government, nor a president. Also unlike the US system, government jobs in Athens were filled by lottery each year. Women in Athens could not vote. Students may point out that in both Athens and the United States, the practice of democracy grew over a period of years. Just as in Athens, the United States at one time did not allow women to vote. The paragraph is written with correct use of conventions (grammar, punctuation, capitalization, and spelling).

3 A **good** paragraph has a main idea or topic sentence and at least two or three supporting detail sentences. It presents a well-balanced comparison of the practice of democracy in ancient Athens and in the United States, listing areas in which the practice of democracy was similar, and in which it was different. The paragraph is written with generally correct use of conventions.

2 A **fair** paragraph presents information on the practice of democracy in ancient Athens and in the United States, although in some cases the comparison between the two may not be complete, focusing instead on only one society or the other. The paragraph may include some errors in the use of conventions.

1 A **poor** paragraph contains inaccurate information about the practice of democracy in ancient Athens and in the United States.

0 An **unscorable** paragraph is incomplete or does not relate to the task.

Performance Assessment

Chapter 13: Writing About Perspective

Goal

The student will write a paragraph from the point of view of an ancient Athenian on whether women should participate fully in Athenian democracy.

Suggestions:

1. Review Lesson 2 and have students point out the role citizens played in the government of ancient Athens.

2. Model the process by reading the relevant parts of Lesson 1 to students on the restrictions imposed on upper-class Athenian women.

Portfolio Opportunities

Have students exchange paragraphs with their partners and evaluate the paragraphs by completing peer assessment forms. Then have students place their paragraphs in their portfolios with the peer assessment forms.

SCORING RUBRIC

4 An **excellent** paragraph provides an accurate description of the limits of women's participation in Athenian democracy and a thoughtful opinion on why women should or should not be allowed to participate in it more fully. The paragraph describes the different jobs citizens took in government (such as generals or jurors) and gives a detailed reason on why a woman should or should not perform that job. The paragraph is clearly written from the point of view of an ancient Athenian. It is written with correct use of conventions (grammar, punctuation, capitalization, and spelling).

3 A **good** paragraph provides an accurate description of the limits of women's participation in Athenian democracy and an opinion on why women should or should not be allowed to participate in it more fully. It describes one or two government jobs performed by citizens in ancient Athens, with a reason why a woman should or should not perform that job. The paragraph is written from the point of view of an ancient Athenian. It is written with generally correct use of conventions.

2 A **fair** paragraph provides an opinion on why women should or should not be allowed to participate in Athenian democracy, but does not mention any of the specific government jobs. It may not be clearly written from the point of view of an ancient Athenian, and may include some errors in the use of conventions.

1 A **poor** paragraph contains inaccurate information on women's participation in Athenian democracy and does not include a clear opinion on the issue.

0 An **unscorable** paragraph is incomplete or does not relate to the task.

Performance Assessment

Chapter 13: Writing a Profile

Goal

The student will write a profile of Alexander the Great, discussing his character and achievements.

Suggestions:

1. Review Lesson 3 and have students discuss the accomplishments and character of Alexander.

2. Model the process by sharing with students a profile of another historical person.

Portfolio Opportunities

Have students complete self-assessment forms and have them place their profiles and the completed self-assessment forms in their portfolios.

SCORING RUBRIC

4   An **excellent** profile provides a description of Alexander's character and military accomplishments. The profile will include the following points. Alexander was an intelligent, well-educated man who had a love of Greek culture and traditions. He was also a courageous and respected soldier, who would ride in the front line in a battle. His military accomplishments include the conquest of most of Greece and the Persian empire. The profile will also note, in detail, that Alexander's accomplishments extended beyond the military. His victories helped spread the Greek language and culture throughout Europe. The profile is written with correct use of conventions (grammar, punctuation, capitalization, and spelling).

3   A **good** profile describes Alexander's military accomplishments in detail and goes on to include a discussion of his character. It notes that Alexander's accomplishments went further than military conquest. The profile is written with generally correct use of conventions.

2   A **fair** profile describes Alexander's military accomplishments in some detail and may include aspects of his character. His influence beyond military conquest may not be included. Some information may be inaccurate, and the profile may include some errors in the use of conventions.

1   A **poor** profile does not reflect an accurate understanding of Alexander's character and accomplishments.

0   An **unscorable** profile is unreadable, is not a profile, or is not related to Alexander the Great.

Performance Assessment

Unit 5 Project: Perform a Scene about Life in Ancient Times

Goal
The student will work with members of a small group to create and perform a scene about an ancient civilization.

Suggestions:
1. Have students choose a civilization from the unit and discuss ways to research more information about it.

2. Model the process by giving an example of what a scene from an ancient civilization might involve.

Portfolio Opportunities
Have students perform their scenes for the class and evaluate the scenes by using the questions on the peer assessment form. Then have students place the script of the scene and the peer assessments in their portfolios. For individual assessment have each student complete a self-assessment form to evaluate his or her contribution to the project.

SCORING RUBRIC

4 An **excellent** project depicts a scene from an ancient civilization. It shows what daily life was like or portrays an event, and it reflects the results of thorough research. The scene includes a character for each group member, and each part has at least five lines to speak. The scene is presented well, characters wear appropriate costumes, and there is some scenery evident. The dialogue is written with correct use of conventions (grammar, punctuation, capitalization, and spelling).

3 A **good** project depicts a scene from an ancient civilization. It shows what daily life was like or portrays an event, and it reflects some results of research. The scene includes a character for each group member, and each part has three or four lines to speak. The scene is presented well, characters wear appropriate costumes, and there is some scenery evident. The dialogue is written with generally correct use of conventions (grammar, punctuation, capitalization, and spelling).

2 A **fair** project depicts a scene from an ancient civilization. It shows what daily life was like or portrays an event, but it may not reflect the results of any significant research. The scene includes a character for each group member, and each part has two or three lines to speak. The scene is presented somewhat smoothly, but it may not include appropriate costumes or scenery. The dialogue may include some errors in the use of conventions.

1 A **poor** project may depict a scene of some kind from an ancient civilization, but it does not show what daily life was like or portray an event. It does not reflect the results of any research. The scene does not have a coherent dialogue and does not include appropriate costumes or scenery.

0 An **unscorable** project is incomplete or is not presented as a scene.

Performance Assessment

Chapter 14: Writing an Explanation

Goal

The student writes two paragraphs explaining how Rome's republican government worked and comparing and contrasting it with Athenian democracy.

Suggestions:

1. Review Lesson 2 and have students discuss the structure of Rome's republican government.

2. Model the process by giving an example of one aspect of Rome's government and contrasting it with Athenian democracy.

Portfolio Opportunities

Have students exchange explanations with their partners and evaluate the explanations by completing peer assessment forms. Then have students place their explanations in their portfolios with the peer assessments.

SCORING RUBRIC

4 An **excellent** explanation has a main idea or topic sentence and two supporting paragraphs, and it presents information in a logical order. One paragraph explains the three branches of Rome's republican government and their functions. The second paragraph gives one or two comparisons and one or two contrasts between Rome's government and Athenian democracy. Examples: Rome's republican government had three branches. The Senate was controlled by the patricians, or nobles; it determined how Rome would act toward other governments and controlled all the money collected and spent by the Republic. The citizen assembly elected tribunes, who fought for fair treatment and equal rights for plebeians. The third branch consisted of two elected consuls who served as army commanders and judges. Rome's government was different from Athens' democracy in that it was a representative government. Instead of having all citizens voice their opinions, people elected representatives to speak for them. In Athens every citizen had a single but equal vote; in Rome the value of the vote was based on the person's power and influence. The explanation is written with correct use of conventions (grammar, punctuation, capitalization, and spelling).

3 A **good** explanation has a main idea or topic sentence and two supporting paragraphs, and it presents information in a logical order. One paragraph explains the three branches of Rome's republican government and their functions. The second paragraph gives one comparison and one contrast between Rome's government and Athenian democracy. The explanation is written with generally correct use of conventions.

2 A **fair** explanation has a main idea or topic sentence and two supporting paragraphs. One paragraph explains the basic principles of Rome's republican government, and the second paragraph gives one contrast between Rome's government and Athenian democracy. The explanation may not present information in a logical order, or it may include some inaccurate information. The explanation may include some errors in the use of conventions.

1 A **poor** explanation does not reflect an accurate understanding of Rome's republican government.

0 An **unscorable** explanation is incomplete or does not relate to the task.

Performance Assessment

Chapter 14: Writing an Interview

Goal

The student writes an interview with a person in ancient Rome.

Suggestions:

1. Review Lesson 2 and have students discuss the different classes of people who lived in Rome.

2. Model the process by reading an excerpt from an interview.

Portfolio Opportunities

Have students evaluate their own interviews by using them to role-play with partners and discussing what is good about them and what might be improved. Then have students share their interviews with the class and place the interviews in their portfolios.

SCORING RUBRIC

4 An **excellent** interview has at least five well-written questions that are easy to understand, are specific to a Roman individual, lead to informative responses, and are presented in a logical sequence. For example, the interviewer might choose a plebeian citizen and ask for an example of the treatment of plebeians by the patricians. The plebeian might respond that the patricians were unfair because they did not write down the laws that they created which made it difficult to know what was or was not against the law. He might further state that he was one of many plebeians who were protesting this injustice. The questions and answers in the interview are clearly labeled and the interview is written with correct use of conventions (grammar, punctuation, capitalization, and spelling).

3 A **good** interview has at least four well-written questions that are easy to understand, are specific to a Roman individual, lead to informative responses, and are presented in a logical sequence. The questions and answers in the interview are clearly labeled and the interview is written with generally correct use of conventions.

2 A **fair** interview has at two or three well-written questions that are easy to understand, are specific to a Roman individual, and lead to informative responses. The questions may not be presented in a logical sequence, or they may include questions that are not appropriate to the topic. The responses may include some inaccurate information. The questions and answers in the interview may not be clearly labeled and the interview may include some errors in the use of conventions.

1 A **poor** interview does not have clear, focused questions and does not lead to informative responses.

0 An **unscorable** interview is unreadable, is not written as an interview, or does not have anything to do with a Roman individual.

Performance Assessment

Chapter 14: Writing About Perspectives

Goal

The student will write a paragraph that sums up what he or she thinks two different Romans would have thought about Rome.

Suggestions:

1. Review Lesson 2 and have students discuss the different roles that these people played in Roman life: a slave, a patrician woman, Hannibal, Scipio.

2. Model the process by contrasting how Hannibal and Scipio might have viewed Rome.

Portfolio Opportunities

Have students evaluate their own paragraphs by completing self-assessment forms. Then have students place their paragraphs and self-assessments in their portfolios.

SCORING RUBRIC

4 An **excellent** paragraph has a clear main idea or topic sentence, and at least four supporting detail sentences. It realistically describes the perspective of each person and explains why the person would have his or her point of view. Information is presented in a logical order. For example, the paragraph might show how a slave hated Rome, felt that he or she was denied rights, was treated unjustly, and generally thought that Rome was a bad place to be. The paragraph is written with correct use of conventions (grammar, punctuation, capitalization, and spelling).

3 A **good** paragraph has a clear main idea or topic sentence, and three or four supporting detail sentences. It realistically describes the perspective of each person and explains why the person would have his or her point of view. Information is presented in a logical order. The paragraph is written with generally correct use of conventions.

2 A **fair** paragraph has a main idea or topic sentence, and at least two supporting detail sentences. It describes the perspective of each person and explains why the person would have his or her point of view, although the explanations may contain some inaccurate information. The paragraph may include some errors in the use of conventions.

1 A **poor** paragraph does not reflect an understanding of Roman life.

0 An **unscorable** paragraph is incomplete or does not relate to the task.

Performance Assessment

Chapter 15: Writing a TV Report

Goal
The student, as a TV reporter sent back in time, writes a report on Julius Caesar's assassination for the evening news.

Suggestions:
1. Have students review Lesson 3 and discuss how they might present a TV report about Julius Caesar's assassination.

2. Model the process by showing a videotape of an evening news report.

Portfolio Opportunities
Have students work with small groups to present their reports and evaluate the reports by completing peer assessment forms. Then have students display or videotape their reports or place them in their portfolios with the peer assessment forms.

SCORING RUBRIC

4 An **excellent** report has a strong topic sentence and three or more supporting detail sentences that present information in a logical order. The report reflects the results of research, describes the assassination of Caesar in detail, and uses language that is viewer-directed. Details about the assassination tell who, what, when, where, and why. Caesar was killed by his enemies in the Senate on March 15, 44 B.C. He was stabbed to death in the Senate building because other members of the Senate resented his taking over Rome and ruling as a dictator, and because they felt that he was destroying the republican traditions of Rome. The report is written with correct use of conventions (grammar, punctuation, capitalization, and spelling).

3 A **good** report has a topic sentence and three or more supporting detail sentences that present information in a logical order. The report reflects the results of research, describes the assassination of Caesar in detail, and uses language that is viewer-directed. Details about the assassination tell four of the five Ws. The report is written with generally correct use of conventions.

2 A **fair** report has a topic sentence, although it may not be clearly stated, and at least two supporting detail sentences. The report describes the assassination of Caesar and uses language that is viewer-directed, although it may not present information in a logical order. The report reflects some results of research, and it tells three of the 5 Ws. The report may include some errors in the use of conventions.

1 A **poor** report does not describe the assassination of Caesar in any significant detail, or it presents generally inaccurate information.

0 An **unscorable** report is incomplete or is not related to the topic.

Performance Assessment

Chapter 15: Writing Biographical Paragraphs

Goal

The student will write a brief biography about two of the following people: Augustus, Paul, or Constantine.

Suggestions:

1. Review relevant sections of the chapter and have students discuss the lives of each person.

2. Model the process by reading an excerpt from a biography about one of these people.

Portfolio Opportunities

Have students work in small groups to exchange their paragraphs and evaluate the paragraphs by completing peer assessment forms. Then have students place their paragraphs in their portfolios with the peer assessment forms.

SCORING RUBRIC

4 An **excellent** paragraph has a clear topic sentence and at least four supporting detail sentences. It describes important aspects of the subjects' lives, shows how they affected or influenced other people and the history of Rome, and is arranged in a logical order. Example: Constantine became emperor in 306 and reunited the empire. He established a new capital in a Greek colony, which he renamed Constantinople. Influenced by a dream in 312, Constantine became a supporter of Christianity, and this led to the growth of the religion. Under Constantine, Christian churches began to be built. The paragraph is written with correct use of conventions (grammar, punctuation, capitalization, and spelling).

3 A **good** paragraph has a clear topic sentence and at least three supporting detail sentences. It describes important aspects of the subjects' lives, shows how they affected or influenced other people and the history of Rome, and is arranged in a logical order. The paragraph is written with generally correct use of conventions.

2 A **fair** paragraph has a clear topic sentence and two supporting detail sentences. It describes one or two important aspects of the subjects' lives, although it may not be arranged in a logical order or may contain some inaccurate information. The paragraph may include some errors in the use of conventions.

1 A **poor** paragraph contains inaccurate information and does not reflect an accurate understanding of the subjects.

0 An **unscorable** paragraph is incomplete, is not a biography, or does not relate to any of the three people.

Performance Assessment

Chapter 15: Writing a Comparison

Goal

The student will write a paragraph describing the decline of the Roman empire and comparing the problems of the western empire with the successes of the Byzantine empire in the east.

Suggestions:

1. Review Lesson 3 and have students discuss reasons for the decline of Rome.

2. Model the process by giving an example of one reason for the decline.

Portfolio Opportunities

Have students evaluate their own paragraphs by completing self-assessment forms. Then have students place their paragraphs and self-assessments in their portfolios.

SCORING RUBRIC

4 An **excellent** paragraph has a clear main idea or topic sentence and at least three supporting detail sentences. It describes at least three reasons for the decline of Rome and at least two comparisons between the western and eastern empires. Examples: The Roman empire was becoming too large to control, and armies from northern Europe were beginning to attack parts of the empire. As communications and tax collections faltered, the army weakened and the empire became poorer. In A.D. 284 Diocletian divided the empire into two parts. As he took control of the eastern part, power began to shift to the east. When Constantine took power, he focused his energies in the east and Constantinople became the center of the empire. Rather than punishing or executing Christians, he allowed Christians to worship freely. As northern Europeans took over more of the western empire, the eastern empire became stronger. The paragraph is written with correct use of conventions (grammar, punctuation, capitalization, and spelling).

3 A **good** paragraph has a main idea or topic sentence and at least three supporting detail sentences. It describes two or three reasons for the decline of Rome and one or two comparisons between the western and eastern empires. The paragraph is written with generally correct use of conventions.

2 A **fair** paragraph is related to a main idea or topic, but the main idea may not be clearly stated. It describes two reasons for the decline of Rome and one comparison between the western and eastern empires, but information may not be presented in a logical order. The paragraph may include some inaccurate information and may include some errors in the use of conventions.

1 A **poor** paragraph does not explain the decline of Rome, or it presents generally inaccurate information.

0 An **unscorable** paragraph is incomplete or is not related to the decline of Rome and the rise of the Byzantine empire.

Performance Assessment

Unit 6 Project: Make a Famous People Game

Goal

The student will work with a partner to create and play a game about famous people mentioned in the unit.

Suggestions:

1. Have students brainstorm a list of people mentioned in the unit and decide by themselves which people they will cover.
2. Model the process by giving an example of a famous person and a fact about the person.

Portfolio Opportunities

Have students exchange games with other groups and evaluate the games by using the questions on the peer assessment form. Then have students display their games and place the peer assessments in their portfolios. For individual assessment have each student complete a self-assessment form to evaluate his or her contribution to the project.

SCORING RUBRIC

4 An **excellent** game has a set of 12 index cards naming famous people from the unit and 12 index cards giving important facts about each person. Each fact card has a clear and accurate detail about the person, the detail and the person can easily be matched in the game context, and the text on the card is written with correct use of conventions (grammar, punctuation, capitalization, and spelling).

3 A **good** game has a set of 12 index cards naming famous people from the unit and 12 index cards giving important facts about each person. At least ten of the fact cards have clear and accurate details about the people, the details and the people can easily be matched in the game context, and the text on the card is written with generally correct use of conventions.

2 A **fair** game has a set of 12 index cards naming famous people from the unit and 12 index cards giving important facts about each person. At least eight of the fact cards have clear and accurate details about the people. Some of the cards may include inaccurate information, and the text on the cards may include some errors in the use of conventions.

1 A **poor** game has a set of fewer than 12 index cards naming famous people from the unit and fewer than 12 index cards giving facts about each person. The fact cards are not detailed or clear enough to match with the people, or the fact cards give generally inaccurate information.

0 An **unscorable** game is incomplete or does not relate to famous people in the unit.